BEFORE YOU START READING, DOWNLOAD YOUR FREE BONUSES!

Scan the QR-code & Access
all the Resources for FREE!

https://dl.bookfunnel.com/h8hzy33mn7

The Self-Sufficient Living Cheat Sheet
10 Simple Steps to Become More Self-Sufficient in 1 Hour or Less

How to restore balance to the environment around you... even if you live in a tiny apartment in the city.
Discover:

- **How to increase your income** by selling "useless" household items
- The environmentally friendly way to replace your car — invest in THIS special vehicle to **eliminate your carbon footprint**
- The secret ingredient to **turning your backyard into a thriving garden**
- 17+ different types of food scraps and 'waste' that you can use to feed your garden
- How to drastically **cut down on food waste** without eating less
- 4 natural products you can use to make your own eco-friendly cleaning supplies
- The simple alternative to 'consumerism' — the age-old method for **getting what you need without paying money for it**
- The 9 fundamental items you need to create a self-sufficient first-aid kit
- One of the top skills that most people are afraid of learning — and how you can master it effortlessly
- 3 essential tips for **gaining financial independence**

The Prepper Emergency Preparedness & Survival Checklist:
10 Easy Things You Can Do Right Now to Ready Your Family & Home for Any Life-Threatening Catastrophe

Natural disasters demolish everything in their path, but your peace of mind and sense of safety don't have to be among them. Here's what you need to know...

- Why having an emergency plan in place is so crucial and how it will help to keep your family safe
- How to stockpile emergency supplies intelligently and why you shouldn't overdo it
- How to store and conserve water so that you know you'll have enough to last you through the crisis
- A powerful 3-step guide to ensuring financial preparedness, no matter what happens
- A step-by-step guide to maximizing your storage space, so you and your family can have exactly what you need ready and available at all times
- Why knowing the hazards of your home ahead of time could save a life and how to steer clear of these in case of an emergency
- Everything you need to know for creating a successful evacuation plan, should the worst happen and you need to flee safely

**101 Recipes, Tips, Crafts, DIY Projects and More for a
Beautiful Low Waste Life**
Reduce Your Carbon Footprint and Make Earth-Friendly
Living Fun With This Comprehensive Guide

Practical, easy ways to improve your personal health and
habits while contributing to a brighter future for yourself and
the planet
Discover:

- **Simple customizable recipes for creating your
  own food, home garden, and skincare products**
- The tools you need for each project to successfully
  achieve sustainable living
- Step-by-step instructions for life-enhancing skills
  from preserving food to raising your own animals
  and forging for wild berries
- **Realistic life changes that reduce your carbon-
  footprint while saving you money**
- Sustainable crafts that don't require any previous
  knowledge or expertise
- Self-care that extends beyond the individual and
  positively impacts the environment
- **Essential tips on how to take back control of
  your life -- become self-sustained and
  independent**

First Aid Fundamentals
A Step-By-Step Illustrated Guide to the Top 10 Essential
First Aid Procedures Everyone Should Know

Discover:

- **What you should do to keep this type of animal attack from turning into a fatal allergic reaction**
- Why sprains are more than just minor injuries, and how you can keep them from getting worse
- **How to make the best use of your environment in critical situations**
- The difference between second- and third-degree burns, and what you should do when either one happens
- Why treating a burn with ice can actually cause more damage to your skin
- When to use heat to treat an injury, and when you should use something cold
- **How to determine the severity of frostbite**, and what you should do in specific cases
- Why knowing this popular disco song could help you save a life
- The key first aid skill that everyone should know — **make sure you learn THIS technique the right way**

Food Preservation Starter Kit
10 Beginner-Friendly Ways to Preserve Food at Home | Including Instructional Illustrations and Simple Directions

Grocery store prices are skyrocketing! It's time for a self-sustaining lifestyle.
Discover:

- **10 incredibly effective and easy ways to preserve your food for a self-sustaining lifestyle**
- The art of canning and the many different ways you can preserve food efficiently without any prior experience
- A glorious trip down memory lane to learn the historical methods of preservation passed down from one generation to the next
- **How to make your own pickled goods**: enjoy the tanginess straight from your kitchen
- Detailed illustrations and directions so you won't feel lost in the preservation process
- The health benefits of dehydrating your food and how fermentation can be **the key to a self-sufficient life**
- **The secrets to living a processed-free life** and saving Mother Earth all at the same time

Get all the resources for FREE by scanning the QR-Code below:

Off-Grid Living 2022–2023

A Step-by-Step, Back to Basics Guide to Become Completely Self-Sufficient In as Little as 30 Days With the Most up-to-Date Information

Small Footprint Press

Table of Contents

INTRODUCTION... 1

    WE HEAR YOU 2
    SOMETHING BETTER 3

CHAPTER 1: IS OFF-GRID LIVING THE RIGHT CHOICE FOR YOU?
.... 7

    WHAT IS OFF-GRID LIVING? 8
        Green 9
        Self-Reliance 10
        Privacy 11
        Investment 12
    HOW DO I KNOW IF OFF-GRID LIVING IS FOR ME? 14
        Self-Starter 14
        Autodidact 15
        Able to Follow Through on Commitments 16
        A Love for Nature.. 17
        Healthy and Fit 17
    START SMALL 18
    MINDSET AND ATTITUDE 20
        Kids 24

CHAPTER 2: LOCATION, LOCATION, LOCATION 26

    HOW TO FIND THE PERFECT OFF-GRID LOCATION 27
        Soil 27
        Climate.. 28
        Growing Season... 29
        Water... 30
        The Law.. 30
        Taxes and Exemptions 33
        Cost of Living 34
        Natural Disasters 35

Homeschooling *36*

Access to Civilization *36*

BEST STATES FOR OFF-GRID LIVING... 37

North Carolina *38*

Michigan *39*

Tennessee *40*

Indiana *41*

Iowa *43*

Virginia *44*

Oregon *45*

Missouri *46*

Wyoming *47*

Idaho *48*

A FEW GREAT SPOTS OUTSIDE OF THE U.S. 49

Raoul Island, New Zealand *50*

Lasqueti Island, Canada *50*

Khula Dharma, South Africa *51*

OFF-GRID HOMES 53

Fair Warning *54*

Cabin or House *55*

Yurt *56*

Vehicle *57*

Shipping Container *58*

Micro Home aka Tiny House *59*

CHAPTER 3: OFF-GRID WATER SYSTEM...............................60

CLEANING... 61

RAIN... 63

WELLS 64

Shallow Well or Pump Well? *65*

Deep Well *66*

SPRINGS, RIVERS, AND CREEKS 68

DELIVERY AND PICKUP.. 69

STORAGE 70

CHAPTER 4: GENERATING OFF-GRID POWER 72

POWER SOURCES AND SAVING.. 72

SOLAR.. 74

Wind 77

Geothermal... 78

Micro-Hydro 79

Gas-Powered Generator.. 80

Storage 81

CHAPTER 5: OFF-GRID NUTRITION 85

Growing Food 86

    Gardening 86

    Raising Animals 91

Foods to Grow/Stock up On................................. 100

    Dry Seasoning and Salt................................... 105

    Dehydrating, Salting, and Smoking 105

    Pickling and Canning 107

    Cooling.. 107

How to Feed Yourself Without Power.................. 109

    Wood Stove 109

    Solar Oven... 110

    Propane 111

    Grilling 111

    Earth Oven 112

Living off the Land 113

    Don't Eat Wild Mushrooms 114

    Hunting.. 114

    Fishing... 116

    Trapping 116

CHAPTER 6: HEATING AND COOLING YOUR OFF-GRID HOME
.. 118

Heating and Cooling... 119

    Geothermal.. 119

    Passive Solar Design 120

Heating Your Home 123

    Wood Stove 123

    Compost Water Heater.................................... 125

    Radiant Heat Floor.. 126

Cooling Your Home 127

    Air Conditioning.. 127

Solar Chimney *128*
Solar Fans *129*
Sun Oven and Outdoor Fires *130*

CHAPTER 7: OFF-GRID WASTE MANAGEMENT **131**

Trash and Composting 131
Trash *133*
Burn *134*
Gray Water 135
Septic System 136
Outhouse 137
Composting Toilet 137

AN OUTLINE TO START YOUR NEW HOME **140**

CONCLUSION **148**

One Last Thing 149

REFERENCES **152**

Introduction

Over the past year, there has been a sudden and powerful interest in leaving the cities and finding an independent life in the country. You probably feel those feelings, too. After all, you are reading this book. Well, you're not alone. There's been a massive exodus from some of the densest population centers in the United States. We have seen net population losses and places like New York, Nairobi, and Paris.

People are just sick of it. They're sick of the noise, the pollution, and the chaos.

People are leaving for places that have natural beauty. In Russia, people are leaving for country estates called *dachas*. In the U.K., people are leaving London and Edinburgh for the Scottish highlands. People are abandoning San Francisco and New York. We are watching a great migration from cities worldwide. After 2020, people don't want to feel confined anymore. People want to be able to walk outside freely. They don't want to feel dependent on strangers. They don't want to live every day feeling like they need permission.

It's no surprise then that so many people have been recently attracted to living off the grid. Living off the grid offers relief for many people who have been suffocating with those feelings and are ready to get out.

Cities are strange environments that we've created for ourselves. We could have made any kind of place to live, and for some reason, we chose to stack ourselves into tiny little apartments, 40 stories tall. We decided that this was worth paying $1,800 in rent every month.

New York had the good sense to set a bit of land aside and put some nature there, with Central Park. City planners had the foresight to know that if people were separated too much from nature, it would crush their spirits and make them feel crazy.

Now we are at a time where we don't even remember why we wanted to live like that. Lots of people are seeing it for the first time.

We Hear You

The people at Small Footprint Press know exactly what you're feeling. Our company was founded by people who felt the same way. That's why we wrote this book—there are people all over the world looking for some help.

Our mission is to empower people: to teach them to prepare themselves and their families for the challenges that come, so they can live their life securely, without fear.

Small Footprint Press is dedicated to a cause of a sustainable future, making the world a place where people not just survive but also thrive.

For that reason, we are happy to offer this book as a guide to help like-minded people live the best life they can. As part of our commitment to this cause, we donate proceeds from every website order to help protect our planet.

Something Better

Think of this book as a shopping catalog. You're building a new life, and you need to figure out all the pieces and how you're going to put it all together. The title of this book promises that you can live off-grid in 30 days. We absolutely stand by that. However, what that off-grid life looks like is entirely what you make it.

This is a primer to get you started; there is a lot more to learn. If you want chickens, you'll need to learn all you can about raising chickens. If you aren't going to raise chickens, then don't bother. Everyone has their personal needs, and we can't cover all of them in just one book.

In this book, we will cover a lot of the things that you know you don't know and many things that you don't know that you don't know. Get it?

Living off-grid simply means that you are living in a home that isn't connected to public infrastructure. That means you aren't connected to the electrical grid, the municipal water supply, sewage system, or telephone.

Some people enjoy living a very simple, primitive type of lifestyle that uses as little modern convenience as possible. Other people can live a completely normal modern lifestyle off the grid. You can find a place anywhere in between. If you want to live in a super minimalist, 18th-century lifestyle, that's fine. If you want to live a totally modern lifestyle off-grid, that's fine, too. It's just a matter of what you are looking for.

This book will cover a lot of topics, but it can't teach you everything you need to know. This one book can't train you to be a plumber, electrician, outdoorsman, carpenter, and farmer. What this book can and will do is give you a broad understanding of living off-grid, giving you the information and options to help you decide what's best for you and your family.

One topic that a lot of people might be interested in but we won't get into is prices. Prices are changing all the time. Wind power and solar technology are improving and becoming more popular, so we're seeing price decreases as it becomes more popular in the consumer market. Battery technology is getting better. There are also changes in the price of inflation and some recent political considerations that will affect the availability of imports.

For that reason, We're not going to tell you what things cost. By the time you read this, it's maybe totally different. You are going to want to do your own shopping and figure out those costs on your own. While some things are cheaper, and there's no reason to pay more for them, some things you get are exactly what you pay for. Suggesting you get the most expensive Gucci may not be appropriate and also saying you should get the cheapest one available might be a terrible idea.

Chapter 1:

Is off-Grid Living the Right Choice for You?

Living off-grid isn't for everyone.

There are some purists we'll say any connection to the grid means you weren't living off of the grid; we don't need to pay attention to them. There are levels of off-grid living. Between living in a tiny, cramped apartment in The Laurel on Manhattan's Upper East Side and living in a log home that's a 90-minute journey to the nearest grocery store, there is a wide spectrum. Imagine this book as a collection of tools and ideas with which you can build the life that you want.

Don't let that purest call you a phony. The words off-grid living are just words to describe a particular lifestyle. Don't hold on too tightly to the identity of it. This is about you living your best life and using your own self-reliance and will to create that life.

Living off-grid is all about self-reliance and self-determination. You have to be aware of nature and what it provides.

This isn't always easy, and it isn't for everyone, especially when just starting out. There are so many things to learn and so many trials that will challenge you along the way. Living on your own, developing your self-reliance, and learning to take control of all of your own needs is not the easiest way to live a life but it is a rewarding one. It's one thing to work a job that pays you good money and make enough for a down payment on a home to live and maybe raise a family. There's another experience entirely of living in a home that you built.

What Is off-Grid Living?

It's very simple. Living off-grid means living a life disconnected from public and private utilities. That means you are disconnected from:

- the electrical grid.

- gas.

- municipal water supply and sewage.

- telephone lines.

It doesn't mean living without the things that those services provide. It means providing them for yourself.

Living off-grid does NOT mean:

- living in a medieval hut.

- abstaining from modern conveniences.

- cutting off contact from the outside world.

- growing a beard and living in a bunker, writing a weird manifesto.

You can do all those things if you want, but they don't have anything to do with off-grid living. There are many reasons why a person would choose to live off the grid. This is a lifestyle that attracts all kinds of people from all kinds of backgrounds. Ask yourself if any of these apply to you.

Green

Disconnecting from the grid means disconnecting from the energy system. Being able to produce your own energy from the sun, wind, and water is a way to reduce your impact on the environment. Perhaps you just want to separate yourself from the pollution of the cities.

Many people living off-grid have objections to the factory farming practices and would rather grow their own food than participate in the industrial food system. Plenty of people feel better knowing exactly where their food came from because they grew it themselves. They can grow what they like, and they always know it is free of GMOs and pesticides.

We're all aware of the electricity we spend in our homes. There's also the electricity that you don't see on your power bill every month. That electricity is factored into the price of every manufactured thing you own. Some of those items are manufactured abroad in places that have few environmental laws. Many of the things you own may have been built or manufactured using coal or oil energy, which are well-known pollutants. If you reduce your consumption by using the land, you can also reduce your dependence on the things that you don't agree with.

A self-sufficient lifestyle might help a person be more conscientious about their own footprint and impact on global climate change. Many people have gotten into off-grid living as part of a movement of self-directed environmental personal responsibility. You probably can't change the world, but you can change yourself. If enough people do that, then we're all a lot better off.

Self-Reliance

There are plenty of people who simply like to be self-reliant. In the event of some terrible disaster, self-sufficiency will not be a problem for a person living off-grid. If the power goes out, they have power. If the water becomes a problem, they have water. If the cost of food spikes or there are shortages, that's not going to be a problem for a family who raises their own.

Overall, people just feel a sense of pride and accomplishment. Some people generally don't want to feel like they are a burden on others and that no other person is a burden on them. There's a certain kind of sense of security that you gain when you know that you don't need to rely on other people. If you only need to rely on yourself, and you are reliable, then you'll never be disappointed.

If you are the kind of person that wants to strike it out and make it on your own, and to build something that you can be proud of, homesteading might be something for you.

Privacy

Lots of people like privacy: They like quiet and solitude. If you are the kind of person who's inclined to walk around your house in the nude, you can do so without worrying about any neighbors peeking into the windows. In fact, you could probably just walk outside completely nude without any fear of phone calls to the police.

If you want to have guests over, play music, and have a bonfire and a good time outside, there is no one close enough to you to be bothered to complain. No one is going to come and knock on your door and tell you to keep down the noise.

Likewise, you don't have to deal with anybody else's noise. People in the city are accustomed to a lot of ambient noise. They have to hear traffic and cars honking their horns. The occasional car alarm goes off for no apparent reason at 1:00 a.m.; colicky babies screaming so loud that you can hear them through the walls of your apartment; and barking dogs, bravely protecting a homeowner from the dangerous pizza delivery guy who just arrived.

Being isolated can also isolate you from the problems in the city. If you live in a place with a lot of crime and violence, that tends to stay very local. Having a place relatively isolated is less likely to be targeted, so long as the owner takes the right precautions.

Investment

You don't have to be a hippie or a bearded mountain man to live off-grid. Sometimes, it just makes financial sense. A large off-grid project can have a big upfront cost, but over time, it can easily pay for itself from the savings on electric, water, gas, and food bills. Living off-grid may simply make sense for people trying to be thrifty.

If you buy or build a home in a very remote location, it may be way too expensive to get utilities out to your home. For completely practical reasons, connecting to the grid might just be unrealistic for you—this is more common than you might think. Homes built very high in the mountains or deep into the woods or country, without many neighbors, might decide that off-grid living is considerably less expensive than paying to have pipes and electrical lines built all the way to the grid to hook it up.

People who are investing in homes also often build off-grid sites to rent out to vacationers. Many people don't want to live in a remote place, far away from it all, but many people would love to vacation at a place like that. Making a remote and rustic off-grid location as a rental or vacation destination through one of the online hotel alternative websites could be a very remunerative enterprise.

Developing an off-grid home can require a good chunk of change. However, all of that money is an investment. Every addition you develop adds to the value of the land and will come back to you when you sell— provided there is no terrible disaster, knock on wood.

There's been an increased interest in leaving the cities in the last year and people escaping into rural areas. One can probably expect that the value of the land is going to increase over time and not decrease. For that reason, having a self-sufficient and isolated spot that appeals to people trying to escape city life could be a valuable property to flip.

How Do I Know if off-Grid Living Is for Me?

Frankly, it might not be. Off-grid living is not for everybody. It takes a certain kind of personality to take on a project and commit to it. It takes a lot of self-reliance and eagerness to learn.

People have become very accustomed to convenience. Convenience is another word for time—as in saving time. Anything convenient saves time, but there is also a cost. Fast food is convenient. Ordering cheap things online is convenient. Sometimes, there are things more valuable than convenience. Also, the time that we are trying to save is just being wasted on other frivolous things.

These are some qualities that might determine if you are the kind of person who can do it. You don't need all of them, one is enough, but the more, the better.

Self-Starter

If you like projects, this is a great way to live. You will never run out of things to do. Many people make their home into their primary hobby. Are you the kind of person who is thinking about a good way to fix a squeaky garage door? Or the kind of person who builds a shed? If you're the kind of person who loves keeping busy and loves to work with their hands, you are in luck.

There are always new ideas you have for additions and for upgrades. Once your home is all put together, you'll start imagining other things you could build such as a sauna or a guest house. Once you get done with those, maybe you consider what it would take to build an artificial pond. If this sounds like you, keep reading.

Autodidact

That's not a type of dinosaur: An autodidact is a person who teaches themselves. You will need to learn a lot to live off-grid. If you don't like learning, this lifestyle will not work for you unless you learn. Learning is always going to be important.

Starting this life will make you a jack of all trades very quickly. To achieve absolute self-sufficiency, you will have to learn plumbing, electrical, farming, animal care, local law, and many other skills. Some people see that and want nothing to do with that. Others see a list like that and get excited.

This book is just the start of your off-grid education. There are many more resources that you will need to avail yourself of. Within a year, you'll know so much, you'll barely remember living another way.

If you like learning and are a very curious person who enjoys figuring things out and discovering new things, you will have plenty of opportunities. You will discover all the things you didn't know that you needed to know, and there are a lot.

Able to Follow Through on Commitments

You were meant to be someone who isn't a quitter. Depending on how you develop your land, there can be a large initial investment. It's totally possible to get started with $10,000, but depending on some factors, it could cost more. If you aren't serious about it, then you could easily waste a lot of time and money.

Pioneers and homesteaders of previous centuries did it with a lot less than we have available. Lucky for you, there are more tools and technologies available to you than they had.

By definition, you won't have an infrastructure around you that has been built up over a century by thousands of people who were financed by governments and corporations. You have to develop your own infrastructure from the bottom up. Over the long term, it can pay for itself.

This isn't like a month-long free trial at a gym or using a subscription service for a phone app. It's not the kind of thing you can half do by half measure. If you are a person who likes to finish what they start, and someone who doesn't rush into things, you have the right personality to live off-grid.

A Love for Nature

Last but not least, if you are looking to live off-grid somewhere that is far away from other people, you should be a person who genuinely loves nature. You are going to be surrounded by a lot of it.

Living off-grid means living in tandem with nature. You have to work cooperatively with it. Mother Nature decides when it rains, when the sun shines, and when the wind blows. While not everyone feels comfortable feeling at the mercy of nature, other people don't feel like they are at nature's mercy, but rather they are adapting to what nature prescribes. It's a very different attitude.

Maybe you really like living in a city where it's easy to find things that you need within a five-minute drive, and you don't like the unpredictability of nature. If you like gardening and animals, you'll have plenty of time with them. If you are someone who loves hiking, skiing, fishing, hunting, exploring, then this is where you want to be. Are you someone who loves campfires and loves to have their morning coffee on a porch overlooking a beautiful landscape? If so, you have come to the right place.

Healthy and Fit

People who have medical issues that require regular treatments and need to be close to the hospital or visit a clinic regularly are at greater risk if they live far away. Being off-grid doesn't mean that you can't be close to a hospital, but if you need a hospital to be close, be sure to factor that in. If you are planning on doing the work yourself, you should be healthy and able. People who are confined to wheelchairs might have a very rough time with it. However, if you're in a wheelchair and can build yourself your dream home, that would be very impressive and inspiring.

If you aren't strong or have good cardio, that problem will solve itself. You'll be chopping and carrying wood, building a fence, and all the other physical activities, plus a cellar without junk food—that will get you in a fitter state in no time.

Start Small

Living off the grid also doesn't have to be 100% complete on day one. Sometimes, the smartest way to start is to start small. Once you have a good piece of land that has all the features you need, you can get a trailer for relatively cheap to park there. That's a good place to start.

You can buy any water you need and bring it to your location. If you're ready now, just go and do it. Take it one step at a time. For most water systems, you'll need a pump. That means you'll need power. Power comes first.

You can start with a gas-powered generator until you can set up something more permanent. It won't be very long before you've set up your sustainable power system such as using solar power. Once that's up, you won't need a generator, then you'll be off the electrical grid.

You may have just put out some rain barrels to start with, and that's fine. That'll help supplement any water that you are purchasing. When you get a well or more-developed method of getting clean water, you can stop buying it. Then, you'll be off the water grid.

You can rely on the grocery store when you begin and slowly phase that out as you build your garden and greenhouse, and build a coop to raise some chickens. Then you'll be self-sufficient for food.

There's no reason to start with the expectation that you will be completely self-sufficient on day one. Frankly, that's very unrealistic unless you can afford to have people come and completely design your project from the ground up before you even move in.

Start small and build out. Develop what you need to as you go.

As we say later on in this book multiple times, there is so much to learn. The best way to learn new things is to do them, so don't overwhelm yourself with tons of projects. Find one goal that you can accomplish and work on that. When it's done, continue to the next thing. If you come across any problems along the way, you'll figure those out and learn how to fix them, too. By the time you've moved to your next project, you'll already be an expert in whatever you just resolved.

As the subtitle of this book promises, you can live off-grid within 30 days, but you cannot build a gigantic off-grid compound with every luxury in 30 days. We don't know if it's possible to lay the foundation, build a house, and install plumbing and wiring in just 30 days. In some places, we don't think it's even possible to get a permit for construction within 30 days.

However, you can begin the moment that you have land. If you start small, you can be out there next month building toward something, so if you want to do it, sincerely, just go do it.

Mindset and Attitude

The off-grid mentality requires a balanced view of optimism and pessimism. You will need optimism to do the work and to believe in yourself that it can be done. It also needs pessimism because you will need to understand that things will go wrong—things that you cannot predict, and things that you should be able to anticipate. Your mantra should match that of the Scouts of America: Always be prepared. Just because your electricity is working doesn't mean that something won't happen to stop the electricity. Just because you have a car and you can leave doesn't mean that car will always work. Something happens to the car, and there is an emergency that requires you to get yourself or someone else to live with to a hospital, what is the plan B? If plan B fails, what is plan C?

The problem is that you can't anticipate, so you are going to have to figure that out. There are things you want to anticipate because you simply didn't know. You read this book and probably visited websites, read articles, and watched videos on the Internet, but there are things you know you don't know, like the weight of 14 ounces of mercury. There are also the things you don't know that you don't know. You can only learn these things when experience places them in front of you, and without any preparation for them, you will have to adapt and be creative.

Attitude and mindset are intangible things that you need to equip yourself with.

One thing to keep in mind is what it means to live isolated or far away from other people. If you are from an urban or suburban area, there are a lot of things that you take for granted. You have to understand what it means to be self-reliant in the context of living far away from people.

One thing to remember: If something goes wrong on your property, you are the first line of defense. If something that breaks down, you are the closest person to be able to fix it. You're not going to be able to rely on a landlord to come and have a look at it later the same day. If you need professional help, you're going to have to call them up, and they're going to have to drive out to you.

If you're a good distance away from town, you're going to want to have big trips. That means any kind of shopping you want to do, you should just choose a day and get everything done all at once—that means buying and bulk and getting lots of stuff. That means also thinking well in advance about what you will need, not just what you want for dinner tonight. You can't just go downstairs to the Bodega and pick up a sandwich. When you go to town, be sure to maximize your time and get plenty of supplies.

If you were injured, you might be a good distance from a hospital. For this reason, we strongly recommend that everyone get some kind of first aid training but especially if you live far away from the nearest emergency room. Living alone far away from other people can be risky. If you are not healthy or if you're not doing well, then you probably should have other people with you just in case. Something like a heart attack is a problem or much less lethal if you can expect an ambulance to arrive within seven minutes. However, if the nearest ambulance is 29 minutes away, you might be in for a lot of trouble.

This also means self-defense. When you live in an isolated area, the chances that someone is going to come and mug you, break into your house, or rob you are lower. However, if someone does try to come to your house with intentions, the police may be very far away. For that reason, you are going to be your own first and last line of defense. That could be surveillance cameras or security lights that detect motion. That could mean being armed. The point is, if it's just you out there, it may mean that nobody's coming to help.

Not having stores and other people available to you quickly means that you need to do what survivalists do. Any person who's into wilderness survival will tell you that you need multiple redundancies. That means if one of your pieces of equipment fails, you need to have a backup. When you are building your system, you are going to want to integrate multiple redundancies throughout it. That means multiple overlapping systems. If you can get electricity from two or more sources—if one of those sources goes down—you'll always have another one as a backup. If you can get water from more than one source, if you have a problem like a pump failing, then it won't be nearly as bad. This is especially true if you are totally relying on a car. If something goes wrong with your vehicle, and you need to leave the property in a hurry, you aren't going to have a ride-sharing driver just down the block, so you want to make sure that whatever vehicle you use is in tip-top condition, and don't leave anything to chance.

You have to think ahead more than you would living in a city. You have to think further in the future about living without your food and about possible problems with your water and power. You have to think about your own health and safety. When aid is always really close, you don't have to think about these things that much. When there's always a grocery store a couple miles away, you don't think about storing your food to last through the winter. A huge part of living an off the grid mindset is not preparing for the worst—not because it's likely but because something bad always happens eventually. Like the various Scouts of America say, always be prepared.

Kids

Going off-grid as a single person or with a spouse has certain natural advantages. You only need to care for the needs of two people. Going alone is dangerous because if something were to happen to you, no one is going to come looking for you. Someone is going to wonder why you didn't go back home.

Having children with you living off-grid has a lot of advantages and a lot of difficulties tied up with it. Well, children do have the power to contribute more and more as they grow older, and when they're very young, they consume more than they produce. A six-year-old can help out in small ways, but they need more help than they can give. Around the time a child is 10, and then in an off-road living environment, their contributions to the family and the consumption should be about breaking even. So, for the first decade of human life, they need more than they give. This means that adults need to produce more than they need to cover the distance. Adults produce their plus, and the rest goes to the children. This has been a fact that's been with us for the entirety of our species and before.

Plus, what is crucial in raising kids is education. Depending on how off the grid you are living in, you might not have realistic access to schools. You might have ideological disagreements with how the schools are handled because of religious or political differences. Maybe you just think that you can educate your children better than a state employee. Those things are true, you're going to need to homeschool your kids. Maybe you are perfectly happy with the education system, and you have an easy way for your children to go to school and come back. That's perfectly fine. You know what is best for your kids and family better than anyone else.

Chapter 2:

Location, Location,

Location

Living off the grid also means living off the land. The place you select will have more impact on your off-grid lifestyle than any other factor.

Living off the grid is dealing with the uncertainty of nature.

Choosing a place is a tremendous commitment. If you are going to put all the work into making a place be sustaining, it needs to be the right place. You don't want to put a lot of time, money, and energy into something only to realize that it can't work for you. You need to really plan ahead. If you are close with your family, then being far apart from them might be a deal-breaker.

Location will determine a lot about the way you live. Your access to water, the soil, and other natural features will inform what energy and sources are available to you. The laws can be as important, if not more important, in determining how you get your water, how you get your electricity, how you heat and cool your home, and even what you eat. Make no mistake: Choosing where you live is going to be the most important decision, and there are a lot of factors that you need to balance.

How to Find the Perfect off-Grid Location

What is important to you will ultimately depend on you. No one can tell you better than you what your needs are and what kind of life you prefer. As we said in the introduction, this book is like a catalog of options that you can choose from.

Soil

If you are going to be doing any farming, the quality of the soil is going to be very important. You don't want to try to put in all the energy into starting a farm on land that won't give anything to yield. An easy way to determine if the land is good is just to simply look around. Are other people farming in this area? If they are, there's a very good chance that they know what they are doing and are using farmland.

This isn't a deal-breaker by any means. If the soil isn't great, you can buy soil at any home improvement store, you can add your own nitrogen, and use your compost to keep the mineral-rich earth. You can build a garden using raised garden beds for vegetables and herbs, using your own earth.

Not all locations are appropriate for certain kinds of farming. Depending on the season, soil, and climate, certain crops will be more amenable than others. You aren't likely to find very many tomato farmers in Alaska, for example.

Climate

Maybe that should go without saying but the climate is going to be crucial to how you organize your life. When living off-grid, you are dependent on nature to provide for you. Different climates have different advantages and disadvantages that you will need to weigh to make the life that you want.

Warmer climates are usually good for planting, however, you will have to deal with the problem of cooling yourself and any animals that you have. It's much harder to cool down than it is to warm up.

Likewise, wetter climates usually mean more water. They also mean humidity, which isn't great for humans, but it is nice for plants. Humidity also usually corresponds with plant growth. A lot of plants can block the wind and sun, which can make generating electricity more difficult if you're relying on solar and wind.

A nearby pond might be a great place to draw water and to raise fish. It might also be a potential breeding ground for mosquitoes.

Dry environments tend to be more comfortable. Arid areas also usually have more sun and wind, which is great for generating power. However, it may mean that getting water is more difficult or more expensive. Getting water is very important. Humans consume a lot of it, and your plants and animals will, too.

One very simple and important consideration is if you can even get onto your land. If your home is far away from the nearest road and you have lots of snowfall, you might be at risk of getting snowed in, and unlike other people who live in the city and subdivisions, there is no truck already on its way to plow the snow for you. Having a long road and heavy snow could mean you'll need a truck that you can mount a snowplow onto.

That's a lot of double-edged swords. There are advantages and there are drawbacks to everything. You have to seriously consider and weigh what is right for you.

Growing Season

Tied to climate and soil is the growing season. If you are going to be heavily reliant on producing your own food, you are going to want a longer and more productive season. You probably won't be doing that much growth during the winter. Historically, farmers plant in the spring, grow in the summer, harvest in the fall, and rely on their surplus during the winter.

Building a greenhouse can maximize productivity and extend the season if it is short. The more you grow and effectively store, the deeper you can fill your pantries and enjoy those supplies throughout winter. Luckily if you run out of food, you still have the option of driving to the local grocery store.

Water

The importance of water cannot be understated. When living in an arid place like parts of New Mexico and Australia, people are absolutely dependent on the water infrastructure. There is very little rainfall and very little access to natural water supplies.

Without water, you cannot drink; maintain plants or animals; take a shower, cook most foods; or wash your clothes or dishes. You absolutely need water, and getting water is your most important and most difficult task.

Your primary ways of getting water will come from a well, supplemented by rainfall. If you are lucky enough to have rivers or creeks that pass through your property or a pond—provided that there are no regulations against using that water—you can use those as well.

The Law

This is the least fun and interesting part of off-grid living, but it is very important. Making an error about the law can cost you a lot of money and trouble down the road. There's no use using common sense because laws often don't make sense. Don't assume that you are doing it right without checking first.

Between different states, there will be completely different regulations regarding building structures, digging wells, hunting, fishing, and every other thing that you can imagine. The number of laws is so vast and complex, we even have an entire profession to simply argue about what the laws actually are. They're called lawyers, and even they need to specialize in very specific areas of the law because there are so many.

If you aren't sure if something you were doing is legal or not, we strongly recommend that you don't just guess. You need to investigate for yourself. Reach out to any local boards or administrative offices that handle that sort of thing—that means the DNR or the mayor's office. Even if they can't help you, they may be able to point you toward someone else who can.

Another useful resource is people who are also living the lifestyle already that you are working for. They have probably already experienced legal hiccups along the way, and if you can reach out to them, they can save you a lot of trouble. Look around on the Internet for forums and groups that are into off-grid living. If you can find others who live in a particular area, they might have answers to your questions.

Never ever buy land in a subdivision. Subdivisions are parcels that are pieces of land, part of a larger covenant agreement. If you have land that is attached to such an agreement, that means you are going to have a lot more rules that you need to follow. This is like having a homeowners' association and a bunch of neighbors who might have very strong opinions about what you do with your land. This isn't just true in the suburbs. You can also find properties like this in rural areas, so be sure to avoid this.

Keep in mind that agriculturally zoned land tends to be cheaper than residential or commercial land. If you can, buy agricultural land, and make sure it allows for ownership of livestock and farming. If you buy land that is zoned incorrectly, you might find that a lot of the things you want to do are not legal.

Believe it or not, some counties legally require you to hook up to city water. Whether or not you want to, you can be forced to pay for the installation of the pipes and hook up. This can cost you up to $10,000, or maybe more. This also goes for electricity. Some places legally require you to be on the grid. The whole point is to be off the grid, so don't go buying a place where you are not allowed to be off the grid.

There are also considerations of covenants and regulations about whether or not you can have a camper or trailer on your land and maybe rules about mineral rights or what requirements about a permanent foundation. You might find that a big part of choosing your land is about whether or not you can negotiate the obstacles set up by your state and local government.

Taxes and Exemptions

Tax laws are quite different from state to state. You may have to pay a rather large fee annually depending on the size and location of the land you are using. Depending on your budget, this cost could be an important part of your evaluation about where to homestead. Some places have no income tax; some places have low land taxes. These are things to take into account, depending on your finances.

There are certain tax write-offs that certain states offer that you can avail yourself of. A few states including Oregon and Utah offer tax deductions for using green energy on your property. Some states also offer tax breaks for those who use their land for farming. If you are building a new sizable grow operation, you might find that these rebates are worth your while.

Some states offer what's called the homestead exemption. That means that if you happen to go bankrupt and a certain portion of your land is filed as a homestead, then that portion of your land cannot be taken by creditors. The old traditional form of pharmacy went under during bad times, and workers would ultimately lose their homes—this is a law designed to protect people like that. Maybe you're not terribly concerned about going bankrupt and this is not a factor for you, but it is a nice thing to have all the same just in case.

Cost of Living

Money always matters. You may have a lot, or you may have a little. Your budget is your business, and budgeting might be a crucial factor for you.

Typically, the farther away you are from the city, the cheaper the land will be. People will pay a pretty penny to be close to a hospital or inside a good school district. The farther away you are from all of that, the less you need to spend. You might have to balance how close you want to be to civilization to how much you're willing to spend.

Sometimes, it can be hard to find banks that are willing to finance vacant land. Banks and mortgage companies like to sell you houses, not dirt. Often, the banks that will sell empty land charge more in terms of interest or down payments. One way around this is to work out a deal directly through owner financing. In this case, the bank operates as an intermediary where the lending agreement is directly between the current owner and the prospective buyer. The bank just gets a taste for mediating.

Everyone is living on different budgets and some places are simply more expensive than others. The prices of things are based on whatever the market will bear. Things that you want, such as natural beauty, are also going to be valuable to other people. This is one reason states like Geneva and Southern California are so expensive. Switzerland has access to a beautiful mountain range and nature. California has an entire coastline and beaches galore where you can search. Both have great weather.

Living near people with money costs money.

If you were living in a particularly remote area, things would just simply be more expensive because of the challenge of supplying areas. Areas in or around Alaska or island systems in places like Canada and Southeast Asia can be quite pricey because shipping to them is very expensive and difficult.

Natural Disasters

God forbid that you should experience any serious natural disaster. The odds that your home will be affected by one like that is usually pretty remote, but it shouldn't be ignored. You need to investigate if the area you're homesteading in is particularly vulnerable to flooding, tornadoes, or hurricanes. You need to think about these things ahead and have a plan ready so that you will know ahead of time and have a way to protect yourself.

Communication is important for this. If you live in tornado country, you definitely need access to the national weather service and a place to take shelter, such as a cellar. You want to be the last person to know there's a tornado, with no good way of getting away or taking shelter.

Homeschooling

For people who have kids, or who plan on having kids, school is very important. It matters in terms of quality but also accessibility.

If you are living very far away from schools, you might not have a bus that comes by your home. It might not be realistic to drive your kids to school and back, depending on the distance. Maybe you want to homeschool for ideological reasons.

Whatever the case may be, homeschooling might be important to you. Not all states are equally permissive about homeschooling. You will want to look into this and make sure that your state will allow it if that's important to you.

If you do decide to take the homeschooling route, now is a better time than ever. Homeschooling has come a long way over the last 20 years. There are all kinds of programs and lessons that can be bought online. There are many ways to meet with other parents and children to help them learn to socialize.

Access to Civilization

Some people can't safely live in an isolated area. If you have an illness that requires frequent visits to a doctor or hospital, you don't want to be too far.

Living off-grid does not mean you are living like a caveman or a 19th-century Canadian lumberjack. Being off of a utility grid does not mean being off of a social grid. You don't need to be socially isolated from other people. In fact, any psychologist will strongly recommend that you do not isolate yourself from other people. Just because you are living off the grid never means that you can't go into town to pick up supplies, and it doesn't mean that you can't go out to dinner or sports events.

The distance you are from your closest ER or grocery store might make a huge difference, in terms of driving time, gas, and emergency response. Being in a spot that is difficult for an ambulance to get to might be a deal-breaker.

Best States for off-Grid Living

These are 10 of the best states for living off the grid. This is not a top 10 list, and they aren't ranked from worst to best. Each of these places has its own strengths and weaknesses. Which is "best" depends on your needs and wants. No place is perfect for everyone, but there is a place that is perfect for you.

Look over this list and measure the pros and cons; from there, you can decide which place you feel is best.

North Carolina

"Nothing could be finer than to be in Carolina in the morning." North Carolina is a fantastic farm state, and there are many fellow homesteaders out there on account of their very friendly laws. Plus, since it's a great farming state with a long growing season and very beautiful agriculture, it also happens to be rather expensive. North Carolina is a nice state and you get what you pay for.

Pros

- gig farm state

- lots of homesteaders; ideal out west

- green rebate

- homestead declaration

- long grow season

Cons

- expensive land

- tight on homeschooling

Michigan

The wolverine state is not a bad choice at all. One of its most obvious and valuable features is that there is a ton of fresh water. The state is completely surrounded by enormous lakes, and on the interior are tons of smaller lakes. No one living in Michigan is too far away from a place to take a boat out to relax or to go fishing.

Michigan already has a pretty substantial homesteading community, and you are better off to find plenty of other like-minded people. The more northern in the state you decide to venture, the more open land there is.

One thing Michigan isn't running out of is fresh water. Michigan has all four seasons, although winters may seem a little long. The land is good for raising crops, but the season might be short. Maximize the season.

Michigan is also a great state for fishing. There are more lakes, and you can count plenty of salmon and trout that you can fish.

Michigan also has a large homesteading community. Having people who are also taking on the same project is always a great thing; making friends with others, you can learn a lot. In recent years, the price of living in Michigan has gone up, so take that into consideration.

Pros

- good soil

- short season

- lots of water for fishing

- many other homesteaders

Cons

- laws can be strict

- middle of road taxes

- complicated homeschooling laws

Tennessee

The beautiful state of Tennessee is one of the most underrated in the Union. It also happens to be the state that hosts The Great Appalachian Homesteading Conference. Like North Carolina, Tennessee is a state that is very friendly to homesteaders. While Idaho is getting a lot of love right now, the people of Tennessee should be glad that they haven't been discovered quite yet.

People living off the grid are generally more likely than a lot of people to get nailed with a panoply of natural disasters. Anyone living out there needs to take the proper precautions.

Pros

- mild climate with four seasons

- It's a beautiful state with great state and national parks.

- The cost of living is fairly low—it's about 10% less than the national average.

- There's good dirt for farming, especially in the west.

- plentiful water.

- Rural Homesteading Land Grant

- homestead exemption

Cons

- lots of natural disasters, including earthquakes, tornadoes, and floods.

Indiana

Indiana, like many other places on this list, is great for farming. They've got a good assortment of land and good growing season; they aren't hurting for water. At present, picking up rural land in Indiana may be tricky, so be sure to keep an eye out well in advance if you have any want on moving out there. One last thing, and we say this with all due respect, Indiana, besides homesteading, is a pretty boring state. If you like boring, that's great. If that's going to be a problem for you, maybe look around for other items on this list.

Pros

- mostly farmland

- longer growing season

- good homeschool

- good income tax

Cons

- might be difficult to get land

- high sales tax

Iowa

Iowa is of course a great farming state. They offer generous tax credits for farmers and homestead exemption, which is definitely a big help.

With no disrespect to the good people of Iowa, Iowa is not a very pretty state. It is mostly rolling planes filled with corn, wheat, and soybeans. It doesn't enjoy the beautiful forests of, say, Northern California and Iowa. It doesn't have the mountains of Tennessee and Colorado. It doesn't have beautiful bodies of water like Michigan or Florida. Iowa has many good qualities, but the natural aesthetic is not one of them.

Pros

- big farming state

- tax credits for farm

- homestead exemption

- low tax

- homeschool

Cons

- flooding

- Let's be honest. Iowa isn't very pretty. Sorry, Iowa.

Virginia

Virginia is a fantastic farming state and always has been. They have great rainfall, and they have access to the ocean. It's a very popular state for a good many reasons.

However, the problem with popular states is that they attract lots of people. Lots of people mean more expensive land, higher cost of living, and higher taxes. Unfortunately, that is a lot of the disadvantages of living in a city, except those disadvantages will follow you into the more isolated areas.

Pros

- There's great farming—Virginia is a farming state and always has been.

- good rainfall

- low property tax

- sell back electricity to power

- very popular

Cons

- expensive land

- high cost of living

- strict homeschooling

- disaster prone: hurricanes and flooding

Oregon

Once you get out of the Portland area, you will feel like you're in a completely different country. Oregon is a geologically beautiful state and very wet. Finding water in Oregon is as difficult as throwing a rock and waiting to hear it splash on something. You'll pay a hefty income tax if you make a lot of money, though.

Pros

- no sales tax

- lots of water

- few natural disasters

- green energy tax rebate

- rainy

Cons

- high income tax

Missouri

Missouri is very friendly to homesteads. They are very light with the regulation which is a major hurdle to overcome in more regulated states. In short, it's easier to do what you want with your property. The state is also geologically and vegetably diverse, and one part of the state will be quite different from another one.

Missouri gets a lot of rain. An average of about 40 inches per year, and it is legal to collect rainwater in barrels ("Average Annual Precipitation for Missouri," n.d.). Summers are very hot and can get very humid, but the winters are a little milder. By that, we mean a longer growing season but more need to keep your home cool.

Pros

- long season

- good rain

- good homeschool

- solar incentives

Cons

- rough winters

- high income tax

- natural disasters tornadoes flooding

Wyoming

The cowboy state is a strong option. It is the least populated state in the Union, and the land is pretty low cost. There is plenty of open space for solar and wind. However, sometimes too much of a good thing is a bad thing. Wyoming can have very powerful windstorms that are so strong that your roads are shut down for the safety of drivers. If you are in a location that is vulnerable to wind, you could find yourself in some difficulty. Also, your windmills might be great in most conditions, but powerful winds can sometimes be too much for them to handle.

Wyoming also happens to be a pretty dry state. Between the dryness and the strong winds, that means it also is rather vulnerable to fires. Wildfires are a fact of life in Wyoming.

Pros

- tons of open land

- low cost

- farming

- cheap

- no income tax

- relaxed homeschooling

- good for solar

- windy

Cons

- not much rain and wildfires

Idaho

Idaho might be America's best-kept secret. People who are already living there and know this don't want anyone else to know it, too. They like it the way it is and don't want to see it getting filled up with city people who are fleeing places like Los Angeles and Portland coming in and ruining it. As long as you don't tell anyone that you are from California, they will usually treat you well.

Pros

- Great farmland: A good percentage of the state are people who work in farming. There is a culture around it, and plenty of resources and help are available if you need it.

- Low cost of living: Things are just cheaper there, and they'll stay that way until people realize how great Idaho is.

- Green energy benefits: At the time that this book is being written, Idaho offers tax benefits for people who use green energy.

- Homeschool-friendly options: If you want to homeschool your kids, Idaho won't get in your way.

Cons

- high taxes

- natural disasters

A Few Great Spots Outside of the U.S.

The U.S. is great for homesteading and off-grid living, but it is far from the only country you can go to. There are very innovative and adventurous homesteading communities all over the world. Here are a few of our favorites.

Raoul Island, New Zealand

As anyone who has watched *The Lord of the Rings* movies knows, New Zealand is one of the most beautiful countries on Earth. Raoul Island is a small island with a small population. Almost everyone there lives completely or partially off-grid. The climate is fantastic and you can live in paradise.

Pros

- Off-grid community already there

- Excellent climate

- Unbelievable scenery

- Great fishing

Cons

- Outside supplies need to be shipped in

- Not cheap

Lasqueti Island, Canada

Located in Vancouver, British Columbia, Lasqueti Island is the home to about 400 people in an off-grid community. If you've never been, Vancouver Island is absolutely gorgeous and has everything you need.

Vancouver Island has several privately owned islands, so if you are looking to relocate to an excellent off-grid location, you should probably check them out. They are happy to see any visitors who want to check the place out.

Pros

- Beautiful environment

- Great access to fresh water

- Access to fish

- A community that are already pros

Cons

- It can be difficult to get a work permit in Canada

- It's an island and the only way to leave is by boat or ferry

Khula Dharma, South Africa

Khula Dhamma is an "eco-village," an experiment in green living. People live in updated versions of traditional African huts. Straw and clay make for excellent insulation against Africa's hot climate. This community is self-reliant. They produce their own food, electricity, and water.

Pros

- Anyone looking to be green will love this place

- Very knowledgeable bunch of people

- Inexpensive

Cons

- Perhaps too rustic for some people

- There is an application process to join the community

- Hot

Off-Grid Homes

Living in a home that you built creates a certain intimacy with your environment that's difficult to put into words. People who have done it understand this even if they've never tried to articulate it before.

Imagine you live in a place where every single board is there because you put that board there. Every single nail was hammered into place with your own hands. You know every inch of electrical systems. All the pipes are exactly where you chose to put them. You know how all of these systems work because you couldn't have put them there without knowing it. Better yet, inside of this house are memories of the trials, difficulties, and problems that came along while you were building the home. Each of those memories is a fond one because it is the memory of a challenge that you overcame.

The self-made home contains the story of the conquest over challenges and the pride of doing it yourself. You will live inside of a shrine of your own accomplishments. It's not easy to put a price on that.

There are stories of people who are offered large amounts of money to sell their homes to developers who aren't interested in the home itself but are interested in the land for a larger project. You'll often hear these stories of people who are in their later years, refusing to sell at any price. They're living in a home they built themselves or built by their parents or their spouse. It's one thing to live in a place for a long time and call it home. It's another thing to create a home.

Fair Warning

Before doing any work on your property, it is extremely important that you investigate the laws in your state or accounting to make sure you aren't accidentally breaking any. Every place is different, and there's no reliable way to know what you can and cannot do by just using your own common sense. You may need to purchase permits; you may need to use licensed contractors. We would recommend that you reach out to your local government. Call them, or even better, show up in person and ask them directly.

In one example that we know of personally, a person dug their own well on a property. There was nothing illegal about that, however, for someone to get a bank loan to purchase the property, they needed it to be inspected. During that inspection, they saw that the well was not installed by a person with the state certification. The banks would not loan money to anyone to purchase the property without the certification by the well digger. The owner would have to destroy the well and replace it with another one or find a person who was willing to purchase the property upfront in cash. Needless to say, it was a huge disaster.

Making this mistake can mean that you waste your money with whatever development that you're putting into it; you'll also have to waste money to tear down whatever development you made on the property, and then waste even more money doing it the prescribed way. If you accidentally violate an ordinance, you will be fined over and over until the issue is settled. If you can't settle it, the state could take your land from you to pay off the debts from the fines that you can't pay.

Do not make the mistake of assuming you know what the rules are. Unless you are an expert and have a career developing in that particular area, you need to double-check everything.

Cabin or House

It's the most obvious living situation, and that's why it's the first one. This is going to be the option that most people will go with if they plan on staying on the property long term. Houses are not easy projects, as any homeowner will tell you. When you are adding on the additional challenges of off-grid living, that then means there will be a few other considerations to be mindful of.

Building a cabin has a lot of rewards, though. If you have a family, then you are going to need a place big enough for all of them. If you are laying down roots and really trying to start a life somewhere, this is a good choice. If you are simply trying to improve the land so that you can rent out your property for Airbnb, small rentals, or to eventually sell, building a cabin is the sensible choice.

If you have a big family and need a house, build a house. If it's just you, and you are starting small as we recommended at the start of this book, don't feel like you need to jump into this right away. If you don't need a house, don't get one until you do.

In some rare cases, you might be renovating an older place and retrofitting it to work off-grid. This can be harder than just building a new place from scratch. A lot of off-grid resources are most efficient when they are integrated with the house. It's difficult to build something like a radiant heat floor if the floor is already built. Some old houses might be great candidates for renovation, but I'd recommend against it unless you really know what you are doing.

For the majority of you, you will pay to have a house built, or you will build some of it yourself and hire contractors for other parts. You may not feel qualified to lay a foundation or to install an electrical system. If you are a DIY kind of person and you have the time to do the work yourself, it can be a great experience. If you are an experienced contractor, then you can just continue to the next chapter because you probably already know exactly what you're going to build.

Yurt

For the homesteader who wants to live a more old-fashioned and primitive type of lifestyle, there's always a yurt. Not everyone wants to keep all the luxuries and indulgences of modern civilization—many people would like to get away from those things. These are small, one-room buildings. Some people will build several on their property, so everyone living on the property has their own.

These can be very nice and well done. They are very affordable, cozy, and charming. They're not always great if you would like a lot of privacy from other people you share the property with. They are also a project that is doable for the layperson. A house is a lot, but a nice yurt is within the reach of someone who isn't a pro but would like to make their own home.

Vehicle

Some people like to live in a vehicle. This is a very neat option if you don't like to stay around in one place for very long. If you are in a position in life where you like to travel, you can bring a lot of your home with you. Maybe your land is where you call home, but you move around enough that it just makes sense to live in a home with wheels and an engine. You can have a power system and water system waiting for you when you come home.

Living in a vehicle doesn't always mean living in a camper. There is a large community that likes to refurbish and retrofit large vehicles to live in them. This could just mean something as small as a van, but people have gone as far as refurbishing former ambulances with excellent suspension for traversing difficult mountainous areas. Some people have fixed up vehicles that are out of service or retired school buses and rebuilt them into serviceable homes. There's a tremendous amount of interest in creativity in this lifestyle. Do an Internet search for "van life" and you'll see how popular this trend is, especially with young people.

Shipping Container

It's more common than you may realize, but people have built homes and even larger compounds out of shipping containers—those are those large rectangular boxes made of corrugated steel that they used to ship goods across the ocean.

If you search on the Internet for many of these things, you might be very impressed with what you find. People have designed remarkably modern and interesting homes by stacking containers and welding them together. They look a lot nicer than we are describing them, and obviously, a lot of work is put into them to achieve that. There's also been a recent surplus of shipping containers after the COVID-19 pandemic, so getting them now is cheaper than ever.

One technique is to bury the container mostly with dirt with one end of it open. This essentially looks like a hill with a door in the side of it, like a hobbit's home you would see in *The Lord of the Rings*. The drawback here is that you will need a heavy machine to move that much dirt, and you will not have any windows because it is essentially underground. On the plus side, it feels kind of cool, and it has fantastic insulation. When you are mostly underground, you are essentially using a geothermal conditioning system that keeps your home warmer in the winter and colder in the summer.

Micro Home aka Tiny House

Micro homes are a strange and adorable trend. These are exactly what they sound like: They are super small and very efficiently organized—and very cheap—homes. You can buy a lot of them almost completely put together. Think of them as recreational vehicles without wheels and much nicer overall.

People have also taken tiny houses and built tiny house communities. They are small enough that they can be taken to even tiny plots of land relatively easily. People who live in these are often off-grid and rely on a lot of solar and wind power and rainwater. This is a really great option for someone young and single. This is definitely not an option for people with families who need space. If you can comfortably fit your life inside of a New York apartment, then you can live in a tiny house.

Chapter 3:

Off-Grid Water System

According to the United States Environmental Protection Agency (EPA), the average American family uses 300 gallons of water a day. That isn't a typo. That's 300. 70% of that water is used inside the home and breaks down as follows ("How We Use Water," 2018):

- 24% toilet

- 20% shower

- 19% faucet

- 17% clothes washing

- 12% leaks

- 8% other

The other 30% is used outdoors for washing cars and watering lawns. Needless to say, we use a lot of water.

That number can be cut down dramatically if you are responsible and conscientious, but even if you can manage to cut that number in half, you still need a lot of water.

At a bare minimum, you're going to want 500 gallons of water on hand at any one time. That's water that's already been pumped or collected and stored in a cistern or tank. If you can get more than 1,000 gallons and safely store them, that will make your life much easier. Storing water is crucial for survival, and it can also be important for other systems that your house uses, such as heating.

Cleaning

Before we even get started on collecting water, we must talk about getting clean water.

Clean water is a serious problem in many parts of the world. In the developing world, poor access to water, or water contamination, is a tragedy. For most of human history, finding a reliable source of clean drinking water was very difficult and crucial. This is why ancient cities were always built on rivers for fresh water.

Water straight out of the ground or a pond is not going to be clean. It will have mud, clay, and a lot of other gross stuff you don't want to drink. Wherever you get your water from, you are going to need to include a filtration system—that includes rainwater. Water captured in barrels still probably touched a roof and gutter to be collected. And still water in a barrel is a breeding ground if it isn't treated.

The biggest risk is any form of contamination by microorganisms. If you ingest these, they can seriously mess up your guts. Water can also be contaminated by gas or contaminants that are leaking into the soil.

Do not drink unfiltered water. Water contains all kinds of microscopic organisms that will seriously harm you and potentially kill you.

Simply boiling water kills many different types of contaminants but not all. Most viruses of the bacteria won't survive as they boil. Others can survive it and can only be killed with a very high temperature, usually requiring a pressure cooker. Boiling may be a good enough solution for a short-term survival situation, but boiling water in a pressure cooker is not a good long-term system.

Modern filters are so tight that the gaps in the mesh are measured in fractions of a micrometer. This means most microscopic particulates and organisms cannot get through it. It's also a great way of moving any kind of junk in your water. They usually contain a mix of ceramic and carbon, which are the same thing that they use in the water filters that attach to your sink or use in a pitcher. Filters will need to be replaced, periodically. Consult the instructions of any filter you use.

For your rain barrels, you might want to use tablets. Water purifying tablets kill most biological invaders. Tablets usually use iodine, chlorine, or sodium, so you need to be careful not to overtreat the water. You do not want to be consuming too much of the stuff that cleans the water. Purifying tablets also can't remove any harmful particulates such as heavy metals.

Ultraviolet light can purify water by killing microbes' ability to produce. Light-treated water needs to be used shortly after cleaning or stored in a lightproof location. Normal exposure to light can recontaminate the water.

If you have no access to water, then you have probably chosen a bad place to live. If for some reason you find yourself in a position where you only have access to saltwater, solar-powered desalination is an option.

In short, to get safe water, you are going to have one or more solutions to handle both biological and nonorganic junk.

Rain

Rain is free, easy, and clean. It falls from the sky, and all you have to do is catch it before the earth drinks it. Setting up a series of rain barrels is the simplest way to do this.

You want to use any large surface area as a way to collect. Easy examples are the roof of your home and solar panels. The water can be caught using gutters and delivered into barrels. Just leaving a bunch of barrels out in the yard is not going to be very effective if you want to maximize the space to capture.

As we mentioned earlier in this chapter, barrel water needs to be treated. You absolutely do not want algae or mosquitoes finding a home inside of it.

Rainwater is great but it will not be enough for you. If you live in a very rainy environment and it's just you, maybe you can get away with it—probably not, though. For most people, especially those with children, rain barrels are a very important part of the water system, but they are not enough themselves. Rain barrels are supplemental. They won't be the most important water source.

If you can, have the rainwater diverge directly into one of your main tanks. If you can't do that, you can add the water directly to the tank manually if you don't mind a little bit of heavy lifting. Rainwater can also just be used as a gravity shower.

In the winter, your rainwater is now snow water. If you heat it up, it will serve the same function. It's also much easier to collect because it's all over the place, and you can just scoop it up.

Believe it or not, harvesting rainwater is actually illegal in some places. Make sure you won't get a fine for catching the water from the sky.

Wells

For your main water source, digging a well is by far your best bet. Rain is fine if there's a supplement. Creeks and ponds might not be available or legal to take from. Delivery is fine temporarily, but it's not a permanent solution. If you're going to be living somewhere, you want a permanent, stable, and reliable source of water—that means a well.

Shallow Well or Pump Well?

If there is water high enough, you may be lucky in that you can dig a shallow well. Basically, what you do is get an excavator to dig out a big hole in the ground, about 10 feet in diameter and around 18 or 20 feet in depth. If you're finding water at that depth, you are in luck. I'll keep saying it: Check your laws. Some pumps that go deeper than a precise number of feet are regulated. Yes, the laws are that finicky.

Once you have a hole, you can install the pipe, valve, and pump, and run the pipe up over the top. Then, fill in the rest with gravel, then cover with dirt.

If you are feeling really rustic; you need water now but don't have electricity yet; or if you want a second, minor well, you can always use a lever hand pump— very old-fashioned but very effective for small amounts of water. Not a great way to get water for your whole house, but it's great as an intermediary step or a supplementary system.

Deep Well

One thing that's been a problem with settling new land is finding locations to dig a well. It wasn't that long ago that con artists were making money using dowsing rods, wandering between the town, and promising they could detect places that were good for a well. Then he'd take their money and disappear before the people who hired them were able to realize their mistake.

Any piece of land that you want to dig a well on, you should investigate ahead of time. It would be a good idea to reach out and talk to the neighbors first. See if anyone else nearby has dug their own well. If none of them have, you might be able to speak with folks in the city about any records they have of natural resources. If you are going to need a well, you should use land where you are likely to find water.

Digging a well blind is extremely risky. If there are no other wells nearby and you don't have good information on the water table, you are firing blind.

You may be able to take a relatively shallow well with just an auger and get very lucky. However, in some places, you need to dig and install pipes that are hundreds of feet down. Every single one of those feet costs a lot of money. Maybe you get lucky and you find water 40 feet down. Maybe you don't get lucky and drill down 300 feet and still find nothing. The people who dig the well get paid whether they find water or not.

A well is probably your best source of water, but if you are not careful, you can end up spending a tremendous amount of money with no benefit, so be very careful.

Digging a well may be one of the most expensive projects to get your off-grid home up and running. However, on the plus side, adding a well will greatly raise the property value. As long as you did it with a company following all the rules and licenses, the value added to the land should pay for itself if you ever decide to sell.

Springs, Rivers, and Creeks

If you find a river or creek on your land, you may feel like you have an excellent supply of water. We hate to break it to you, but a lot of states do not allow you to draw water out of creeks, rivers, and ponds crossing through your land. This is doubly true out west. Where water is especially scarce, they have appropriative water rights. That makes it illegal to draw water from a naturally occurring source.

That creak, stream, or river you have somewhere potentially crosses through somebody else's lawn on its destination to some other larger body of water. It would be seriously uncool to interfere with that stream as across as someone else's land. That's why you can't just build a dam and divert the water in another direction. That messes with someone else's property.

If you were grabbing some 100 gallons a year, you might not get caught, but we cannot recommend that you break state law to get water when there are other ways to do it. You may just have to enjoy the calming and serene bliss of the water, but tragically, you won't be able to take a shower with it.

Delivery and Pickup

In survival training, they will teach you that you can go three hours without shelter, three days without water, and three weeks without food. We need to upend that rule a little bit on our priorities. To get water, we need to pump. To get a pump working, we'll need electricity, so electricity is actually more important than water.

If you're developing an area with a hill, you can make things easier for your pump by putting water cisterns on top of the hill and running a line to your house, trenching it, and burying it underground. Natural gravity will give you natural water pressure without requiring any extra electricity.

When you first start your off-grid home, it may be a while before you can get access to your own water. You may be reliant on water from outside. If you have tanks set up and buried, with valves and pumps installed, and pipes going to your home, you can hire a truck to deliver water and fill up your tanks. If not, then you can go to the store and pick up as much as you need and drive it back.

This is not a good long-term solution to your water problems. This is just costing you gasoline and time, plus the water is more expensive than if you were on the grid. You can rely on this kind of water supply for a short time while you are getting your permanent water system fully operational. Also, if there's some kind of problem down the road and you need to do repair on your system or something gets funky, you can get the water delivered if it's the last resort.

We're only including it in this book because realistically you will be using delivered water for a short period at the start of your off-grid homesteading.

Storage

Water needs to be stored. You won't be pumping water every time you turn on a faucet. Water is pumped and stored in tanks as needed. Your indoor water is drawn from the tanks. The bigger the tanks, the more water you have at the ready. You want large volumes of it ready to go.

Like everything else, if you want to be prepared and have more than you need, get it now because you might need it later.

Tanks and cisterns should be stored underground. After just a few feet into the earth, the ground is cool but not frozen. This is important because in the summer, the place under the ground will not begin cooking near water and making it 90 degrees, and in the winter, it won't freeze or burst and become impossible to use.

Any kind of pump system will also need to be underground including the valve. Just like the water, you do not want the mechanics of getting the water out of your pump to freeze—that would be a serious disaster. How much water you'll need and how big your tank is will depend on your personal needs, but we always recommend getting more than you need just to be safe.

Water collected from rain can always be added to your tanks to top them off and give your pump a break.

Chapter 4:

Generating off-Grid Power

Power Sources and Saving

Renewable energy has come a long way, but it isn't a fully mature technology. Like everything in life, there are trade-offs. They have pros and they have cons.

Solar and wind power can generate a tremendous amount of energy when the sun and wind are at their peak. This is great except for one big problem: They create more energy than is needed. The surplus energy can't be stored safely because battery technology hasn't been able to keep pace. When the solar panels aren't catching the sun or when the wind isn't blowing, they produce nothing. We need energy when we need it, not just when nature provides it.

On a municipal scale, this means that green energy still has to be supplemented with other energy, be it nuclear or coal. On a small scale, you can be flexible enough to make it work. Living off-grid means living on an electrical budget. You're going to want to get a good estimate of how much energy you need. If you can get an estimate for how much energy you are using now, you can get a sense of how much energy production you're going to need on your off-grid home.

1,000–1,500W is probably enough juice for your needs, but everyone's needs are different.

The power source you use will depend on your environment. The more you can mix your energy sources, the better. If one isn't generating, another one might be able to make up the difference. Diversity of energy is reliable energy.

Naturally produced energy is about living on nature's schedule. When it offers you wind or sun, you take it while you can get it. If you are using naturally produced power from wind and solar energy, you are living on an electrical budget. You have to regulate your own energy use because you can just use as much as you want and pay a bill for it later.

One way of handling this is by using the power when you have the power. This is called "opportunity usage" and is a very effective way to maximize your power. Schedule all of your heavy electrical activities for when the sun is up and the wind is blowing, and there will be no wasted energy. If you have a washing machine and dryer, and you have a sunny day, that would be an excellent time to do your laundry.

Solar

Solar energy is cheaper and more available now than it has ever been before. It's so common that it's no longer unusual to see solar arrays attached to the roofs of someone's home. Solar panels are made of crystalline silicon wafers. Contact with sunlight causes electrons to move about inside of them, and this flow of electrons is what generates an electrical current.

Big solar farms optimize the energy to drop in the sun by turning the panels automatically to always face the sun and have the optimal angle with more maximum coverage of the surface area of the panels. This is exactly how sunflowers operate—they always move to face the sun so they can get as much sunlight as possible.

Not all solar panels are equal. Some people simply lay them flat on the ground—that is the least effective way of catching the sun. It'll be great and high noon during the summer when the sun is directly above it, but it will be increasingly useless as the sun goes down.

Higher-end models can do what those major industrial solar panels do, and follow the sun. They are definitely more expensive, but they may be worth the initial investment if you can get more juice out of them and optimize your array.

Most people find that installing panels on the roof of the home is the smartest option depending on the way that they face the sun. Many people set up arrays on towers about the property, in areas where there isn't any shade or trees blocking. Very often the best place to put your solar array is in the garden for the same reasons. It's an open space with lots of sunshine.

You can't make a solar panel system without some electrical skills. If you know something about wiring up an electrical system, or you are willing to learn, you can do it yourself. However, it can be risky if you are inexperienced. Faulty craftsmanship can damage some of the systems and cost you money and time.

Building your own system takes planning and research, and, as we say many times in this book, always be sure to check out your local regulations. Some places require permits or official qualifications.

Solar panels also need to be weatherproofed. After they are put up and jointed together, they need to be sealed so that water and moisture do not get into them. Make sure that any panels that you purchase are from a reputable supplier and manufacturer. Getting cheap panels from an untrustworthy supplier could result in a fire. Look around. If something seems so cheap that it's too good to be true, it is. Safety first.

You can build solar panels from scratch out of individual solar cells if you like. It's not too difficult. You start by creating a backing for the panel. You can use a wooden board, and you will need to drill holes and then at the right place so that wires from each cell can pass through the back. They are then wired together using a soldering iron. They should be attached to your backing individually so that they can be removed individually. If a single solar cell is damaged, it should be relatively easy to remove the single damaged cell and replace it without having to replace the entire thing.

A solar panel by itself doesn't do anything without an electrical system. You need to pair your panels with an inverter to turn the direct current (DC) into an alternating current (AC). Nearly everything you use requires AC power. Running DC into that stuff will not work.

Before you even begin designing your system, you should probably get a sense of how much power you will need. Look at your current electrical bill, and you might be able to get an estimate of how much juice you are using. Then, look at weather reports to see how many days of sunshine you get on average in the area that you are building. With a little bit of math, you should be able to get a sense of what the scope of your solar system needs to look like.

For beginners, we recommend that you purchase solar panel kits that come with all the instructions included and all of the tools necessary to build your solar system. Good kits also include racking and a means of mounting your system. If you want to do it yourself but don't really know how, these kits are definitely a wonderful option.

Wrecking refers to installing it to either the ground or onto the roof. If you are using an RV, then you will need to mount it on that. Whichever method you use, these must be very secure; you don't want them falling off or getting blown away by gusty wind. It might be a good idea to get your solar panels from the same place you get your racking supplies to guarantee that they will fit together. Even though some companies promise compatibility, these things can sometimes be like blue jeans. The size on the label says one thing, but when you actually try it on you find it isn't quite what was promised.

Working with a professional who is a trained electrician with expertise in solar panel installation will be likely your best bet. They know all the laws and regulations, they are experts in their field, and they are probably going to get it right the first time. If you are a DIY person who knows a little bit of that electricity and is willing to learn a lot more, this can be a great project for you to take on yourself. If you don't feel up to it, letting a professional deal with it is a good call.

For those living in places like the Pacific Northwest of America or Scotland, catching the sun won't be reliable. You can keep adding panels, but the better choice is to add other energy sources.

Wind

If you live out in the open in a windy place like Argentina, Perth, or Wyoming, the wind is a great option. If you live deep in the woods, you might not get enough wind to make it worth your while. Trees do a great job of breaking up the wind and giving you shelter from hurricanes and dangerously forceful winds. Unfortunately, it also means you can't get wind power.

Wind turbines are commercially available, but they aren't cheap. Some can generate as much as 3,000W— emphasis on CAN. Like solar power, just because the box says it can generate a large wattage doesn't mean that it will. Nature makes that decision.

A lot of areas do not like the look of windmills, and regulate them. Like everything else, check the laws to make sure you're allowed to have them. Windmills also need to be mounted on polls. Usually, higher is better, as there is less obstruction from your buildings, hills, and trees. Around 20 feet should do the trick in most cases.

Geothermal

Geothermal is a very cool option with one major drawback: Getting it up and running can be very pricey.

Geothermal energy is not actually producing electrical power. It just makes heating and cooling easier and more efficient.

Geothermal works by drilling a deep hole in the earth and running water through it. The deeper into the earth you go, the less affected it is by the temperatures on the surface. In effect, the temperature is stable.

When it is ferociously hot outside, the temperature deep in the earth is cooler. When it is intensely cold outside, the temperature in the earth is warmer.

The more you want to change the temperature, the more energy you need. It takes more heat to make ice into a gas than it does to turn liquid water into a gas.

Geothermal works by splitting that amount of energy by meeting your energy need halfway. If you need to cool things down, the geothermal temperature gets you halfway from hot to cold. If you need it warmer, then it's the same thing.

It is very simple, practical, and most importantly, reliable.

This is highly recommended. It doesn't provide electricity, but it makes your electrical systems much more efficient for heating and cooling your home and water.

Micro-Hydro

This is a very interesting option if your spot has running water. Unlike solar and wind, a moving river or creek is always moving. Depending on the time of year, you'll get more or less power, but it's always there for you if you need it.

Reach out to the Geological Survey or Department of Agriculture. They may have data on the speed and force of the water moving through your property. If it isn't strong enough, hydropower might not be worth your time. If your water source does produce enough force, like every other improvement on your land, you should contact whatever local department is in charge of energy or natural resources and ask them about the rules for diverting water.

If you have a green light for those two items, you'll need yourself a generator, turbine, and piping. Consider yourself lucky because this is not an option that is available to most people living off the grid.

Gas-Powered Generator

A generator isn't anyone's first choice, but it's important to include. It uses gasoline—which is expensive and a pollutant—it's loud, and it smells bad. That said, you're going to want one.

You may need a generator to get by while you are getting yourself set up. Until your other power sources are up and running, you will need something.

It's important to have a generator in case of emergencies. Even if you seldom need it, you'll be very happy to have it when you do. As we discussed earlier, several overlapping redundancies are crucial. You'll want a generator just in case. If you accidentally leave your keys in your truck overnight and drain your car battery, you will be very grateful to have a generator.

Important note: Gasoline goes bad. Gas is perishable. It has a shorter life span than you might realize. If you have a spare plastic tank of gas, you will need to change it out periodically. Pure gas that is properly stored can last six months. Gas blended with ethanol lasts three months, so keep this in mind. You don't want to fill a tank with bad gas.

There are options for petroleum-based stabilizers to add to gas, which will extend its life to one to three years.

If your gas looks too dark or you see any sludge in it, it is old, and you can't use it. Putting old or contaminated gas can ruin the machine you're trying to power.

Storage

Energy storage is going to be necessary because the wind won't always be blowing, and the sun won't always be shining. To store the energy, we have two main options.

The obvious answer is batteries. There are lots of options, and not all batteries are created equal. You can get heavy acid batteries, the kind that is used in golf carts. Those are a fine option and relatively cheap, although they are heavy and filled with acid, and you do not want to tip them over because they are full of liquid. You can also find lithium batteries, the same type used in your cell phones. These are cheaper but also more expensive and often have less capacity.

Obviously, you're going to need an electrical system to build these batteries and then to pull power from them when needed into any other electricity you are using in the home.

Battery storage is measured in ampere hours. That means a 100-ampere hour battery will give you 100 amps for one hour . . . sort of. Batteries also have a natural discharge rate. This is called Peukert's law, which complicates the math a little. Batteries have different discharge rates that will also affect how much juice you get out of them. People who know a lot about this will check batteries for Peukert exponents.

The discharge rate can also be affected like the temperature and how old the battery is. This is all complicated stuff, and it actually isn't that important. You don't need to calculate the exact amounts of storage you need. What you need to do is get a rough estimate of what you need and then add on a little bit extra just to be safe.

Energy can also be stored in water. Water is very conductive of energy. This isn't energy you can convert into electricity, but by heating water, you are effectively storing thermal energy. When the sun is shining and you are pulling in a lot of power from your solar arrays, this is a great time to channel some of that energy into your water heater. Tanks with hot water will stay hot for a while. As we discussed, you're going to be pulling more energy in than you need at that time and more than you can store for later. Heating your water during the day is the perfect opportunity to store energy in the water.

Chapter 5:

Off-Grid Nutrition

Eating seems to be one of the most popular topics. That's for good reason: People love food. Plus, when you grow your own food, you have a more personal relationship with it. It's one thing to go to the store and pick up a zucchini; it's another thing entirely to grow that zucchini yourself from start to finish, see the final product, and then prepare it and feed it to yourself and other people.

A lot of people are very concerned about their food. Large agriculture corporations have earned themselves a bad reputation due to their practices of using pesticides and genetically modifying their crops in ways that are trade secrets. It's no surprise then that organic markets and farmers' markets have become so popular. What you eat is very important, and if you are especially alert about these things, there is no better way to know what you are eating than to be the person who makes it.

Growing Food

Gardening

You're certainly going to want a garden. If you aren't using a full-scale farming operation, a garden is a fantastic option. To maximize the value and productivity of that garden, we strongly recommended that you build a greenhouse. Greenhouses are less difficult to make than you might expect and have a few very important effects.

A garden inside of a greenhouse is less vulnerable to animals. If built correctly and securely, you won't have to worry about foxes and rabbits sneaking in and eating your greens.

Plants prefer warmer environments. The greenhouse contains both heat and moisture so that the plants are warm without drying out. The roof and walls protect the plants from the elements. Some plants are very sensitive to heavy rainfall, and several days of bad rain could wreck a garden. Depending on what you are growing ultimately depends on what the optimal temperature is. If you are going to be growing several plants at once, make sure that their optimal temperature overlaps so that all of them can be happy.

You want to keep the greenhouse relatively humid, but try not to break the 90% mark. Too much humidity could lead to mold. Likewise, at night, if things get too cold, humidity can turn to frost and freeze your plants, so make sure that you are maintaining the heat during the night as well.

Every garden should have a few staple items. For a beginner, it's best to stick with plants that aren't too needy. Since you can maximize the heat and water levels, the greenhouse will extend the natural planting season, and you will be able to get more food in one year than you would otherwise.

Vegetables that aren't a terrible amount of work include:

- any kind of hardy root vegetable, including carrots

- basil

- oregano

- tomatoes

- onions

- garlic

- cucumber

- zucchini

- lettuce

- spinach

- bell peppers

- celery

The French chefs reading this book probably noticed that all of the ingredients for mirepoix are present. Many Cajun chefs also noted that the Louisiana variation, "holy trinity," is also included on the list. Needless to say, you know you are off to a good start.

A garden that you plan on living off is a garden that produces all the things that you need to live—that means proteins, fats, antioxidants, and carbohydrates. Skipping out on any of these is not healthy.

If you're making a garden to survive then the nutritional values can be the most important thing. Your staples will include:

- potatoes

- carrots

- beans

- squash

- tomatoes

- onions

- corn

You want to mix and match your garden with foods that take little time to grow and also those that grow quickly. Then you can overlap the cycles of these two and have a constant set of nourishing plants being produced.

Some of the plants that have a short harvest cycle include:

- carrots

- kale

- spinach

- beans

All these will grow to full size within one to two months generally. Potatoes can take three to four months if you are using a spud from some of your older potatoes.

Vegetables don't last long. As soon as you pick them, their clock starts ticking. If you plan on doing a full harvest so that you can replant all of them, make sure you have a plan to consume them or at least a plan to store them. Effectively storing them will be covered later in this chapter.

If you can, you should also get a few herbs growing. A little bit of herb goes a long way, and you can grow most of them very easily. Basil, rosemary, sage, parsley, and thyme are all relatively simple and are excellent in food when they are fresh if you haven't tried it before.

The first part of running a garden is learning how to do it and getting it set up. The nice thing about plants is that most of the growing they do doesn't require much help from you. As long as you put them in a good environment with good soil, water, light, and the right temperature, they do all of the rest of the work.

If you want to get really fancy, you can integrate a greenhouse automation system. This requires a little bit of tactical know-how, but it will save you quite a bit of work in the long run.

By running pipes over your garden with small holes on it, with a time valve, you can have the garden automatically water itself. After the programmed period, water will automatically pump through the pipes and sprinkle the water out of the tiny holes, provided that you put the pipes in the right places. This automatic valve mechanism can be controlled via computer.

Another way to use computers is by ventilating your greenhouse. The temperature inside the greenhouse can't get too hot. Plants like hot temperatures but they have their limits. Using a computer to check the temperature and automatically turn on a fan to start ventilating the greenhouse is a great way of letting a machine do the micromanagement for you.

If you have a greenhouse, that's excellent, but if your garden is going to be too large to use in a greenhouse or you don't want a greenhouse for whatever reason, you are going to need to protect your garden from critters that will want to go in there and enjoy your snacks. Putting any kind of fencing around it so that rabbits and deer don't just wander in and enjoy themselves at your expense is necessary.

Raising Animals

Chickens

Chickens are great. Chickens will produce an egg every other day or so. The daily recommended minimum for protein consumption is about 50 grams. An egg contains about six grams of protein. So a breakfast of three eggs will contain about one-third of your daily required protein intake.

For chickens, you will absolutely need to build them a chicken coop. This usually entails an area fenced in with chicken wire with an indoor little home for them to sit comfortably. You can also let them out during the day—they know where their home is and will return. They'll love to look for bugs in your lawn, but you don't want them out all the time because they are very tasty treats for predators in the wild.

There is an increasing interest in raising home chickens or even ducks. You can find lengthy tutorials on how to raise these animals online. Even in places like Detroit, a lot of people have taken up urban farming projects and created chicken coops in the middle of the suburbs. Now is a great time to get into chicken farming on a small scale. There is so much support and information out there.

Chickens are very stupid and like to use their water as a bathroom. Change the water to make sure they don't kill themselves like that.

Chickens are great for laying eggs, but let us never forget that chickens are also great to eat. If you are raising organic, free-range chickens, you will be getting a very different product than what you might be used to at a grocery store. The ones you purchase at the store have been given growth hormones to make them huge, they get very little exercise, and they only "eat" rain. Your chickens will be considerably smaller but also way tastier. If you don't mind reducing your chicken consumption, you will have some extra tasty chicken as a reward.

A strange fact is that your chickens will seem to spontaneously die sometimes. You won't know why, and you can't afford a chicken autopsy. Don't be surprised when you come to your chicken village and find one of them didn't survive. That's just going to happen.

In any chicken coop, you will want one rooster. You do not want zero roosters, and you do not want two roosters. One rooster is exactly the right amount.

One rooster will be a good defender of the hens. If anyone tries to mess with their hands, the rooster will step in. If there are zero roosters, the hens are out of luck.

If you put two roosters next to each other, they will fight. This isn't a guess—that's what roosters do. The underground animal fighting sport known as cockfighting will happen literally every time you put two roosters next to each other. Roosters love to fight, and they will peck each other to death. Putting two roosters together may as well net you zero roosters.

Fish

If you have a pond or you want to build a pond, you can stock your own fish inside of it. These should be purchased from a decent fishery. You want to make sure that your fish are disease-free so that they won't get each other sick and die. Also, depending on the breed of fish that you were going with, you need to get the male to female ratio right. Otherwise, you might find it overpopulating too quickly, or you might find males fighting with one another depending on the species.

Your fish can be contained within a cage inside of the pond and makes it very easy to scoop them out with a net—not exactly like shooting fish in a barrel but very close.

Pigs

Pigs grow fast and will eat almost anything. They consume a lot of food, around six pounds a day, and will excrete one and a half pounds of waste. Since they'll eat almost anything, they will happily eat all of your leftover foods that are in table scraps, so they never have to go to waste.

Each pig is going to need at least 50 square feet of space and a pen that you build for them. You must keep the food and water far away from each other, optimally at opposite ends of the pen. They have a tendency to defecate near the water. If they start contaminating their own water supply, you're going to have to change it out. It's not good for them to be eating their own waste.

Pigs are very sensitive to sunlight. You can tell because they have very little fur and very light skin. You will definitely want to give them some kind of covering. Pigs usually protect their skin by rolling around the mud, but if they don't have mud because it is a particularly dry time or dry place, then they're going to need something else.

Once a pig has stopped gaining weight, usually at around 280 pounds or more, they are ready to eat. If you know how to butcher a pig or are willing to learn, that's great. Otherwise, you ought to contact a butcher who's close to you who can do that job for you safely and properly.

Pigs are very smart and very friendly. Not the wild ones: They will fight you. However, domesticated pigs are very friendly. There's been a growing trend where people even adopt pigs as family pets, just like dogs, and if you have not spent time around pigs, you may be surprised.

People who did not grow up on farms when they first encountered farm animals have a very different experience. People who grew up around animals and are accustomed to killing them and eating them have a very deep understanding of what meat is and where it comes from. They don't have any illusions about it. When most urban and suburban people see a chicken nugget, they don't think about it as it is.

When you spend time with a pig that you mean to ultimately slaughter and eat, it is understandable if you become emotionally attached. Your experience with animals has been probable that they are either pets or vermin. When the time comes, you might not feel good about killing the animal. There's no special advice on this, we're just warning you that this is a possibility. You can power through the experience and really confront what meat is, or you can decide you can't do it.

Goats

Goats are wonderful for milk, and they don't take up nearly as much room as cows. Some people really dislike goat milk while others think it's really great and are willing to pay a premium for it which is why you may see goat milk and cheese at a higher price at the store. Goats are sensitive to wind, and they need access to shade because they tend to overheat. Be sure to keep your goats and environment where they can keep cool.

Goats are natural lawn mowers. They will graze all day and keep your lawn trim. They can eat several pounds of food for a day just from grass and any hay that you supplement your diet with. They can also drink several gallons of water more or less depending on how much grazing they do, since a lot of their water needs are satisfied by grass.

If you are going to build them a place to live, that's a fantastic idea. They will want a place to sleep and be safe from predators and a place to keep the sun off of them—these shelters should probably be 70 square feet minimum.

There are a lot of things in nature that will poison your goat which they don't know better not to eat. Things like a poppy, stagger grass, and buckwheat are dangerous to a goat, so keep an eye on those.

Goats are also notorious climbers. Even domesticated goats love to climb things. A goat will even climb on top of other animals. Use an image search engine and look for yourself. Keep this in mind because if you have any way for the goat to get onto your roof, they might try to do that. If you are running solar panels on the roof, you probably don't want a goat walking around on them.

Rabbits

Rabbits are a classic option. You cannot survive on rabbit meat alone, however. There's a concept called rapid starvation which is also known as protein poisoning and is caused by the overconsumption of protein with no fat carbohydrates or micronutrients. Rabbits are perfectly fine as are any other lean game so long as you are keeping them part of a well-balanced diet.

Rabbits don't require a lot of space, which is nice. They are extremely good at escaping, though. Your rabbit cage needs to be tighter than Alcatraz, otherwise they will get out. Rabbits are natural diggers, so you'll need to make sure that you have some caging on the ground or floor, so they don't get out that particular way.

Also, rabbits are cute. If you are going to get cold feet and not want to butcher them, that's fine—you can always keep them as pets. However, don't let the rabbit breeding get out of control, which is something that can easily happen if you aren't careful. Breeding is great if you're making food for stew but it's not good when suddenly you have way more pets than you know what to do with. The same situation goes with pigs.

Turkey

Turkeys are an all-American bird, and you can purchase them from a turkey breeder or farm for very cheap. Turkeys are very sensitive animals, and you are likely to lose several of the first few weeks after you buy them. Chicks need to have a warming unit when they are, such as 100–250W lamps. They need to keep the battery at about 100 degrees Fahrenheit for the first week—they want to be toasty. After the first week, they are much less vulnerable, and you can gradually reduce the heat; after a few months, they won't need any heat at all.

Turkeys grow fast, and after three and a half months, they will be big enough that they are ready to be eaten. At 35–45 pounds, they are a lot of food, so be sure to have a way to store the meat properly, or share it with others. There's a reason why a turkey is a traditional bird for Thanksgiving—many people sitting together are all able to share a meal together.

Turkeys are also very smelly. You do not want turkeys anywhere near your house or upwind of it. They also aren't terribly friendly. Unlike some of the other animals, they are not good pets, but they are good food.

Unlike pigs and chickens, there is no way you will get emotionally attached to a turkey. To be perfectly frank, they are mean and their odor is very pungent. If you are maybe squeamish about killing an animal, maybe a turkey is a good way to start because you will not feel bad at all.

Bees

If you have a sweet tooth, you could even consider raising bees. This is an insect that is absolutely vital to the ecosystem and great if you like sugar. Honey is the only known food that never goes bad. There is nothing that you need to do with a container of honey to maintain it. Honey never rots. Honey will retain its edibility longer than you will be alive.

Beekeeping is a very popular hobby. It also has two wonderful side effects: It will produce honey and will pollinate your garden. The easiest way to get started with a beekeeping operation is to purchase the basic starter kits. These are not difficult to find on the Internet. A starter kit usually contains everything you need: frames, a hive feeder, a queen excluder, a smoker, and all your protective gear.

You can keep your bees within a quarter-mile of your garden, and they will do all the work of pollinating your plants. Also depending on where you place them can affect the flavor of the honey. Putting bees next to cloves will add a clove flavor to the honey.

It's a fun hobby and does require some research because there's a lot more to it than you might think. Honey can also be a cool gift. If you put it in a jar and give it to someone, it's a neat and personal thing.

Another by-product of raising bees is wax which can be used for sealing, protecting food to extend life, and making candles.

Dogs

No, we're not suggesting that you eat dog meat! They are just included here because we're already discussing animals. You're not going to eat the bees either.

Dog people are lucky. An off-grid lifestyle is wonderful for dogs. They have tons of space to move around, and they don't need to be taken on walks because there's nowhere for them to run off to.

Dogs also love just to spend time with people while they're working outside, which you will be doing plenty of. Dogs are essentially wolves that were genetically engineered through selective breeding to become home security systems. In a city, you'll find dogs bark at almost any noise that they hear. They bark at people walking by on the sidewalk or another dog a block away that is heading toward the sidewalk. Deep in the country, that response is important. If you are isolated, it's unlikely that you will have unwelcome human visitors, but you can certainly expect unwelcome animal visitors. This could be foxes coming to eat your chickens. This could be a bear simply wandering through. It could be a raccoon who has sniffed out your trash. Whatever it may be, dogs have extremely sharp senses of smell in hearing and will know if you have welcomed visitors long before you do, and they will eagerly tell you about it.

Foods to Grow/Stock up On

Food storage is immensely important. Humans have developed many clever ways of keeping their food clean and safe long before refrigeration.

There are a few foods that are always good to have on hand. Even if you aren't living off-grid, it is just smart to have these in your home.

Rice

Rice has a long shelf life, and if properly stored, rice can last six months or longer. If you also keep it refrigerated, you can get twice as much time out of it. Brown rice is a great source of vitamins and fiber. Brown rice is the most nutritious, and if you're eating to stay alive, just go where the nutrition is.

Price is a staple food for more than half of the planet. That's a pretty ringing endorsement.

Beans

The best friend to rice is beans. This is a well-known and well-traveled survival food. It's also very versatile and can be used in a lot of different ways. Dried beans can be stored for a long time and can be hydrated rather quickly just by soaking and heating them.

Beans are an excellent source of protein, and when complemented with rice, it forms a complete protein.

Nuts

They are an excellent source of protein and fat; dried nuts also store very well.

Cabbage

Yes, cabbage. It is low in calories, but it has a ton of nutrients including B6 and C, and it is very fibrous. It's also very versatile because it can be used in salads. If you are into pickling, you can turn it into sauerkraut or kimchi, which is a great flavor addition and has a very good shelf life.

Corn

It's very easy to grow as long as the soil temperature stays high enough to allow for germination, and you have mature soil. If you can get those two things right, corn is very easy to grow.

Cucumbers

If you plan on pickling, you should have cucumbers. If you are just getting cucumbers for pickling, keep in mind that there is a specific type of cucumber called a pickling cucumber. The ordinary cucumber you're used to that you put on a salad does not work the same way, but you might also like regular cucumbers.

Potatoes

Everybody loves potatoes. It's a starchy crop that's high in carbohydrates, which is important for getting your calorie intake high enough. These are crops that you are trying to live off of, and calories are your body's fuel. Yukon Gold potatoes are probably the best choice.

Sweet Potatoes

Everything we just said about potatoes is true of sweet potatoes. They are calorie dense and have much more iron nutrient content than your average potato. The leafy greens that grow on them are also edible. They have a longer growing season, longer than almost anything else you will be raising. However, if you like sweet potatoes, they might be worth the extra time and effort.

Tomatoes

Setting aside the argument about whether it is a fruit or a vegetable, the tomato is a pretty easy plant as long as you give it ample water. They also like the temperature on the warm side. Tomatoes are great on so many things and can be turned into sauces, added to salads, added on top of burgers, and plenty of other applications.

Lentils

Lentils are packed with protein. It's very difficult to get a decent amount of protein from plant sources: Ask any vegetarian who is conscious of their nutrition. Lentils have around 18 grams of protein per serving—that is the same amount of protein as three eggs. Also, lentils are one of the oldest crops that have ever been cultivated by humans. It is ancient, and lentil soup is just delicious, so if you don't like lentils, start liking lentils.

Spinach

This plant is very easy to grow and packed with vitamins and minerals. For the adventurous, spinach can be stored by freezing it or dehydrating it and then crushing it into a powder. Now you have a powdered nutritional supplement available.

Berries

Everybody loves berries. Raspberries, cranberries, blueberries, or whatever kind of berry. They're all good. They have a lot of nutrition, they have a natural sweetness, and you can do a lot with them. You can turn them into jelly and incorporate them into nearly any dessert item you can think of.

Dry Seasoning and Salt

There's no reason to not make your food taste good even in an emergency or disaster situation. Always have seasoning. There's no good reason not to. Dried herbs and spices last a really long time.

Dehydrating, Salting, and Smoking

For food to go bad, it needs to be wet. Salting food increases the acidity and also dries it out, which in tandem makes bacteria grow much slower. This is exactly why beef jerky was invented. Salted meats have been with humans for as long as we've had salt.

For those who really enjoy food and want to go the extra mile, you should consider building a smokehouse. The process of smoking food adds a wonderful flavor that's impossible to replicate and also dries out the food which helps to preserve it. Smoked salmon, for example, is delicious and a fantastic source of protein.

You can dehydrate meats, but you can also dehydrate fruits. It's also a good idea to put a type of acid on it such as lemon juice or another citrus because the drawing process takes a while. You want to prevent any bacteria from starting a home there during the process.

There are plenty of ways to dry food, including the inside of an oven, or you could have a special dehydrator that uses electricity. One good option is to use a nonelectric dehydrator. It's hard to measure exactly how much time you need to dehydrate any kind of food because depending on your environment, it will change a lot. The outside temperature, humidity, and amount of wind passing through will greatly alter these times. It should take six hours minimum but can take a lot more depending on the thickness and what it is you are dehydrating in the environment. With that being said, you should check in on your dehydration regularly.

Dehydrating doesn't need to use any electricity. Solar dehydrators are a great method, which uses the sun itself to dehydrate. As long as you have a rack to place the food on, make sure that they are ventilated, they are stacked accordingly, and have netting around to keep any bugs off of it, it's not too difficult.

There are many different designs to this sort of thing—one is to create a flat box with a mesh to lay food on then cover it with a metal covering. The sun will heat up the metal, raising the internal temperature. As long as there's proper ventilation underneath it to allow moisture to escape, this is a very simple DIY method.

You can dehydrate beef and fish but DO NOT try to dehydrate birds or pigs. Exposing those kinds of animals to air for longer than is absolutely necessary is extremely dangerous. Do not do it.

Pickling and Canning

There's been a recent new interest in recreational pickling and canning. These are excellent ways to preserve her food. Pickling also has the advantage of adding a vinegar flavor to whatever you want.

You can do just about anything, including meat. Things that are canned need to be sealed properly, so double-check it. Once canned, they need to be stored properly in a cool place without too much sunlight. This could mean a pantry or shed. If you are in a warmer temperature climate, you should seriously consider digging a cellar. The heat of the sun doesn't penetrate very far into the earth, and if you dig down just a short way, you can make a permanently cool space.

If a cellar is too much, it is totally fine if you want to bury your food. A hole in the ground, covered up, will be a natural refrigerator and keep the sun off and hopefully away from animals.

Cooling

Some kinds of foods absolutely need to be stored in a cool place. Some can be left at room temperature, you probably know which ones those are already. According to the FDA, certain foods will require refrigeration and that temperature needs to be 40 degrees Fahrenheit or less. That's very close to freezing temperature. During the winter, you don't need to worry about this that much because if it is already 40 degrees and cold around, then nature is doing your refrigeration for you.

In the summer, you are going to need to find other ways of storing your meat, poultry, fish, dairy, certain cooked foods, eggs, and all the rest.

Certain foods you already know you can leave out are your coffee, bread, onions, honey, olive oil, and potatoes—these are all fine.

The oldest traditional method is to simply build a root cellar. A hole in the ground will be much cooler than the surface or the inside of your home during the summer.

If necessary, you can always go with the old-fashioned route of getting a cooler. If you don't plan on ever storing your food for particularly long, some of the newer and more expensive coolers are extremely good at retaining cold temperature.

If you make a mistake and don't do a good job of preserving your food, look for the following symptoms: nausea, diarrhea, abdominal pain, fever, and vomiting. If you are suffering from one or more of those symptoms, especially if other people in your home are after eating the same thing, you need to reach out and contact medical help immediately—you may be suffering from food poisoning. This can be very dangerous, as it's more than just a stomachache.

Whatever food preservation method or methods you use, don't take any chances with your own health. If food looks iffy, don't take risks.

A really nice, well-insulated chest freezer and/or refrigerator are great. They use less electricity than you might expect, just as long as you don't have kids who like to hang out with the door open, looking at every single thing in the fridge. Don't get a cheap fridge or freezer. A really great, well-insulated fridge pays for itself.

How to Feed Yourself Without Power

Electric ovens crave using as much energy as possible. You cannot use an electric stove, as it is simply not realistic. Likewise, microwaves can be very power-hungry, too. They might be fine to use when you are running at peak energy intake, and you have sunshine and wind, but it's not a great method. Electric stoves are terrible anyway, so nothing is lost. There are plenty more electrically conservative ways to cook that are simply better for cooking.

Wood Stove

If you already have a wood stove in your house keeping you warm, why not cook on it, too? This is a very old and rustic way of cooking food, but it served our ancestors well for hundreds of years. The same fire that's heating up your home also has a flat surface on top. You can simply put a pot on it or a skillet, and do your best to control the temperature by controlling the fire. It's not using any more power than it was before, so there's no reason not to utilize this.

Now it's the middle of summer, so you probably don't want to be having a piping hot fire in your living room. Try to avoid that heat as much as possible; during the summer, you are going to want to stay far away from any kind of fire, and try one of the other options.

Solar Oven

A solar oven is a kind of box with mirrors on the inside and a couple of sides missing. Basically, it's a big shiny device that catches solar energy and then points it into a focal point inside of it. Whatever you want to cook, you simply place it inside the container in that focal point. On a sunny day, this will heat up whatever you are cooking very quickly. Think about when you touch metal on a hot day and how hot that gets.

This type of cooking is probably not great for everything. It is excellent for anything that you need to cook slowly or something that doesn't need to be cooked at a high temperature. For example, you are not going to be cooking steaks or kebabs on one of these things. Instead, any kind of stew would be excellent, or any kind of vegetable that you can cook slowly would be a great way to go. This is a completely green, powerless slow cooker.

There's no way to turn the temperature up or down or to regulate in any particular way, so your best option is to check on a frequency or to place it in such a spot that after enough time, the shadow will cover it and essentially turn it off.

Propane

For cooking, you can use tanks of gas. This is just like a propane tank on a grill that you would use outside. The only difference is that it is a built-in device in your home and also contains an oven. You can't cultivate propane on your own land, which means you will need to purchase it elsewhere or have it delivered.

Gas is great for cooking and is the preferred heating element for the best chefs. It's also relatively cheap if you are just using it for cooking and not trying to heat your entire home with it.

Grilling

Just as simple as that: Everybody knows how to grill, and everybody loves grilling.

If you're using propane to grill, that's going to require you to have propane on hand. If you already happen to have propane running in your kitchen, that is very handy. If you are a charcoal kind of person, that is a great option. Charcoal doesn't go bad. You can store that for as long as you like.

Grilling means great flavor and the outdoor tradition. With a large enough surface, you can prepare a lot of food at the same time. That makes it always a great option if you have a lot of guests or a large family.

If you are raising pigs or you are doing any hunting, a pellet grill is a fantastic option for cooking large amounts of meat. Slowly add in little pellets of wood pulp—they look a lot like hamster food. This keeps feeding a fire at exactly the right amounts to maintain a steady temperature. You can get a slow cooking process going, then you wait 12 hours, culminating in an unbelievably tasty and tender meal the next day, with very little effort.

Earth Oven

Earth ovens are excellent options. You need a slab of stone, and you're going to house that using rocks and dirt to create something like a mound with a mouth on one side that food could be inserted into. Beneath, you can put in some lumber to burn. These things, once they're cooking, get ridiculously hot. The work on it is a very efficient way to insulate the heat, and very little gets wasted even with the open side. If you pop an oven into this, it will be fully cooked in just a few minutes.

During the summer months when you want to keep your home as cool as possible, cooking outside is a great way to make sure that the heat stays outside. From a cooking and aesthetic frame, earth ovens are just cool. You can cook food crazy fast.

They lend themselves to cooking certain kinds of food very well which, if you are into cooking, is a fun culinary experiment. Also, they happen to be very easy to build. Anyone can make one with a few simple instructions. They're all so very cheap because mostly what you need is brick and dirt.

Living off the Land

Depending on your environment and your personal ethics, you can do what people have done for millennia. Nature readily provides protein in the form of animals. Hunting is certainly an option that you can avail yourself of if you want.

This isn't a book about hunting, and we won't go into deep detail about it, but if it is something you're interested in, there are plenty of resources available so that you can learn more about the topic.

States and counties have many laws regarding hunting, fishing, and trapping, and you will need to learn them to not break any laws.

Don't Eat Wild Mushrooms

This should go without saying but some people don't know: Do NOT eat wild mushrooms. We cannot say this strongly enough. We don't care if you have a book on identifying mushrooms. Unless you are a mycologist, do not go putting wild mushrooms in your mouth. Mushrooms can be very dangerous. Even with photographs, the differences between a safe one and a dangerous one can be indistinguishable.

Also, don't eat berries. Don't eat things in the woods if you don't know what you're doing.

Hunting

Hunting with a gun usually has a very short season. There are considerations about what kinds of animals you can hunt during which portion of the season. An average size buck can net you an average of 60 or 70 pounds of meat. A boar can net you double that, which is a lot of meat. You should have some friends or a good way to store it.

If you're using more difficult means of hunting, such as a bow or a black powder rifle, you will have a larger season to hunt in.

If you live in a remote area that has dangerous wildlife such as bears or cougars, having a form of self-defense might be very valuable. Bear spray and other nonlethal weapons are good to have, but if your concern is protecting yourself from a mama bear who feels threatened by you, you're going to want the best tool that you can avail yourself of. This can mean a 10mm pistol at your side or a strong hunting rifle chambered in something like 6.5mm Creedmoor.

Most animals are not interested in you and will not pick a fight with you. However, starving and desperate animals might take their chances; an animal that perceives you as a threat to their young might attack you. These kinds of attacks don't happen often, but when they do, they are brutal. People are torn apart and isolated in the wilderness and unable to easily contact medical aid.

A well-placed shot will kill an animal so quickly that they are dead before they realize what has happened. Taking a bad shot and wounding an animal is a serious faux pas among hunters. Hunters do not want to hurt animals: They want to hunt animals. Wounding an animal is cruel, and tracking a wounded animal to finish the job is not anyone's idea of fun.

If you are interested in hunting but are not experienced, your best bet is to make friends with someone who is. There are a lot of things to learn, not just the laws, of which any good hunter will be well aware. There's also considerations like how to safely harvest what you need, how to most humanely kill an animal, how to stay downwind of an animal, or how to transport the animal after it has been shot. There are many things you should familiarize yourself with before you go walking around in the woods with a gun and no idea what you are doing.

Fishing

Fishing is a great form of recreation and the catch you get will be a great form of protein. If you have access to water that has edible fish, that can be a great asset. Depending on where you live, you might have fishing options all over. You aren't locked to your property, remember. There may be great lakes and streams close enough that you can walk or drive and get yourself a meal—with a fishing license, naturally.

For the truly committed fish eater, you can build an artificial pond and populate it with your own supply of fish. With a river, you can trap fish with zero effort and come by and pick them up as you like.

Trapping

Trapping is a tricky business but has been a staple for eons. Trapping doesn't mean those terrifying spiky metal claws, like bear traps. Those are illegal, so do not use them. If you have one, we don't know where you found one, but don't use it.

Trapping usually means cages and snares. Once again, this is something that depends on your local law, and you need to investigate it before you get involved. The advantage of trapping is that you don't need to do anything other than set up the traps and visit them occasionally. This generates a passive supply of animals without the work of chasing.

It's simply pieces of twine that are attached in certain strategic locations.

If you are tracking, you may be able to find common routes for rabbits. If they find a path that they like, they will keep using it, knowing that it is a relatively safe trail. However, if you know about it, too, it is not so safe for them. A live trap or a snare in one of these spots could nab you a bunny.

If you are the kind of person that isn't squeamish about eating squirrels, just know that they are very easy to catch in a snare. Simply by taking a piece of wood and leaning against a tree, squirrels are lazy like all animals and take the path of least resistance. Squirrels always walk up the branch leaning against the tree which makes a branch the perfect place to leave a snare.

Whatever traps you have on your property, you should be checking them a couple times a day just to make sure to see if anything is there. Snaring and trapping is a game of numbers. The more traps you have set out, the more likely you are to catch any animal.

Snare traps are cheap, but live traps are easy. Just simply get a cage that will close itself when something goes inside of it. Bait that with something the animal of your preference likes and visit to see if anyone took the bait.

Chapter 6:

Heating and Cooling Your off-Grid Home

Heating and cooling are easy to leave as afterthoughts until the moment you need them. If the temperature gets too hot or too cold, you will be miserable. If it gets bad enough, it can be lethal. There are a lot of options here, which is nice.

To be perfectly honest, if a lot of things aren't going great, you can put up with it. If you have to haul your water out or if you can't get your garden running so you have to continue to go to the grocery store, those are all things that you can live with. However, if you are living in a home that is 95 degrees Fahrenheit for a solid week straight, you are going to abandon this project as soon as you can. No one can be expected to live like that when there is a cozy Holiday Inn just 25 miles away.

If your temperature is off, everything else will be off, too, so this is one thing you definitely need to get right.

If you have animals, don't forget them! If you are hot, they are hot; if you are cold, they are cold.

Heating and Cooling

What's better than having a heating system and a cooling system? Having a system that both helps heating and cooling at the same time. Geothermal and passive solar designs are great for all kinds of temperature regulation, both hot and cold. They should be integrated into the home when it's built. Retrofitting a house after the fact might cost you more money and trouble than it's worth. These are integral to the house and are both fantastic systems.

Geothermal

We already discussed geothermal concerning energy in a previous chapter, so we don't want to repeat too much of what was there. Geothermal is outstanding for temperature control because it draws on air that is always cooler than the air when it is hot outside and is always warmer than the air when it is freezing outside.

Geothermal works by running a winding series of pipes underground, then, they draw water through those pipes with a pump that will enter into your home. Sometimes, these pipes will run through the floor and the walls.

The upfront costs can be high, but it is one of the most energy-efficient options for keeping the temperature out of your home comfortably.

After you dig 10 feet under the ground. It's always 55 degrees Fahrenheit, no matter what time of year it is. If it's 100 degrees out, 10 feet down is 55 degrees. It gets to be -10 outside, 10 feet down, it's still 55 degrees.

Geothermal heating system runs water at this temperature and is then able to transmit it to the air using water pumps and fans. This uses some electricity but much less than a standard heating or cooling system.

Depending on the space this can cost several thousands to build, so it will also save a lot of money if you put it together yourself. This isn't too difficult but does require a lot of work.

Geothermal is a very cool system, and there isn't any home that wouldn't benefit from a geothermal system.

Passive Solar Design

Passive solar design is clever architecture and a design of building itself to maximize heat when you need it and minimize heat when you want it to be cooler.

There's a very important mosque in Israel called the Dome of the Rock. It is considered very important and has a very clever design. The mosque is a large stone dome. When the sun rises, it begins to heat up the rock, but it takes a while for this heat to penetrate the stone and reach the inside. By the time it is beginning to heat up the mosque, enough time has passed that the sun is already beginning its descent on the Western horizon. Then, throughout the night, the stone that was used up all day cools, and by the morning, the schedule repeats itself. By simply having a dome of exactly the right amount of stone, it can keep the occupants of the mosque comfortable even in the tremendous scorching summers of the Middle East.

Passing solar design in a modern house uses techniques like this. By choosing exactly where the windows are, facing them toward the sunlight at particular times of day can make an enormous impact. Choosing where to place awnings so that the sunlight will not get in through windows, depending on where it is in the sky, also has a major impact. The particular place you choose to keep a wood-burning stove or trees around the property in the home and how that blocks out sunlight is also a huge factor.

Any kind of passive solar design will be completely integrated with the house. It has to take into account that the direction to the Sun is the height of the Sun during the summer and during the winter. We need to factor in things like the direction that the wind blows. It needs to take into consideration the trees and hills nearby. A good passive solar design will be completely customized for that particular environment, so two houses with passive solar designs will often look very different depending on where they are.

For that reason, passive solar design is a little bit like feng shui. You probably aren't going to know how to do it, and if it's something that interests you, you are going to need to learn a heck of a lot of things before you attempt it yourself. Alternatively, you can reach out and look for architects or contractors who are familiar with passive solar design, and you can help you come up with something that you are happy with.

For the sake of this book, we can't go into too much depth about solar design because that could be an entire book in itself. However, you are encouraged to look into it if you are designing your own home. You can get a lot of interesting ideas that cost you next to nothing but will make your heating and cooling considerably cheaper.

Heating Your Home

Wood Stove

Probably the most popular way to eat your home would be with the classic stove fireplace. These are just lovely to look at, and seeing fire gives off a cozy atmosphere. Many of these can also be used as a stovetop where pots can be placed directly on top to cook with. These things get extremely hot, so this might not be a good option if you have small children.

To operate these things, you also need to clean them regularly, and you will need to get firewood. Firewood can be found, purchased, made, and would need to be kept dry. Wood also needs to be prepared, so large logs should be split into halves, quarters, and thin smaller pieces.

You'll need a chimney, and if you have small children, you will absolutely need a barrier of some kind to keep your kids away. These things get HOT, and no one wants to see a toddler get a bad burn by touching one of these.

They come in all varieties, some very traditional and some very modern. Wood stoves give really warm energy, and we don't just mean heat. They have a certain vibe that they give to a room.

You'll need firewood way ahead of actually needing wood. That means, you need your wood chopped, dry, and in large supply well ahead of when you plan on burning it. Green, freshly cut wood doesn't burn well, and it kicks out sparks. Put your wood someplace dry. Building a barrier over a woodpile to keep the rain off is basically mandatory. Also, you should have your logs already chopped into quarters and smaller bits. The small pieces will be needed as kindling to get the fire going, and once it's cooking, you'll want to be feeding this fire with quarter logs or at least halves. if you are chilling on a cold, winter night, you don't want to have to make a trip outside to chop wood.

Two major drawbacks of the woodfire stove are that they need to be cleaned regularly. You're going to have to get in there with a shovel and remove all of the ash. It's inside your house, so you have to be careful not to get gray dust onto everything. Ashes are a good source of compost, so be sure to add them to anything you want to use to grow.

The other drawback of the woodfire stove is, of course, fire safety. If you aren't careful about managing the fire to a good level and it gets too big or if there's some kind of congestion in the chimney, you can find your house filling with smoke or starting a fire. No matter whether you have a woodfire stove or not, you should own a fire extinguisher. You are probably living far away from any fire department. Everyone needs a fire extinguisher, and that's doubly true if you are building fires inside your home.

Compost Water Heater

Compost heating sounds pretty gross, but if you do it right, don't worry: It won't be gross at all. As organic material breaks down, part of the process is that as microorganisms break down the material, their life cycle releases heat. Compost heating captures this heat and moves it into a conductive source such as water, and then, you can use that water as it is almost warm, or you can pump it through a system to heat up your home.

A compost pile of wood chips can actually put out a considerable amount of heat. You'll notice it because usually these things are left outdoors, and the heat dissipates immediately. A good compost heap gets hotter than you might think.

Running pipes through a compost heats the same way that you would for geothermal, achieving a similar effect. The heat is transferred into the pipe water. The heat is there, all you have to do is capture it. You can also use this water to heat a greenhouse if you are using one or through a radiant heat floor system. You can even find instances of people using it to heat up a hot tub all year. In the last chapter of this book, we'll go into greater detail about how to compost, but for now, it's sufficient to mention that a compost pile will get very hot, up to 150 degrees Fahrenheit. That is much hotter than most people would feel comfortable relaxing in.

Radiant Heat Floor

If you can heat up a lot of water using composting or solar energy, try radiant floor heating. Radiant floor heating looks a lot like compost heating and geothermal but in reverse. The way it works is that hot water is run in piping that zigzags underneath the floor. The pipes touch aluminum plating which is attached to wood. Simply having the pipes making contact with the metal and wood transmits the heat, and a small amount of heat generates upward from the floor. Since heat rises, it creates a general, warm, and ambient temperature. Also because it's just spread out, there are no fans necessary. The heat doesn't just turn on and off based on what a thermometer reads.

A system like this requires a lot of piping and specially made floors. They also need a reliable pump system to keep the water moving.

People spend good money to enjoy heated flooring systems in their bathrooms. These have become very popular with those that can afford them. The radiant floor heating works on the same principle but is much cooler than the bathroom heating. They just heat one room, but you can heat your whole house. Incidentally, if you have a pet cat, they will love this.

Cooling Your Home

It's easier to warm up than it is to cool off. Keeping cool is a very tricky business that has been with humans for the entire history of our species. Our ancestors had to find solutions with much fewer resources and technology than we have now.

One of the considerations for where you choose to live will certainly involve your heat tolerance. Some people feel comfortable in warm environments, and other people just sweat, melt, and feel miserable. Managing your heat is super important. You're going to be feeling pretty miserable if you move out to your new home and are deteriorating in 90-degree weather all summer long.

Thankfully, some options are relatively power efficient and won't require a lot of electricity.

Air Conditioning

One of the greatest modern inventions ever made is the air conditioner. We tend to think of it as a luxury good, but it has had a profound impact on human life.

Water is extremely conductive. That means electricity passes through it easily, and it collects heat easily. Imagine if you put a pot of water in the oven and set the temperature to 500 degrees Fahrenheit, letting it sit for a couple hours. If you were to reach your hand into the oven, you would feel the heat in your hand, but it wouldn't burn you immediately. If you put your hand in the bucket, you would cook your hand. The water is very conductive, but the air isn't.

The way your body manages heat is by sweating. Since water is conductive, and saltwater is extra conductive, the heat stays in the sweat as it leaves the body. The sweat falls off or dries away, carrying the heat with it. Air conditioning works the same way, in principle, using a compressor and an expansion valve filled with refrigerant fluid.

You've seen your electric bills in the summer, so you already know that air conditioners are very expensive to keep running—these are electrically hungry machines.

That said, if the sun is shining and heating you up, they are also feeding your solar systems if you have one. This means that air conditioners are a ripe instance where you can take advantage of opportunity usage, which we covered earlier in the chapter about generating power. If you have enough solar power feeding your air conditioner, the sheets that are making you boil are the exact same energy that is going to cool you down.

Solar Chimney

Solar chimneys work on a very clever principle. You run a black pipe through the roof just like any other chimney, tap it off so that rainfall won't come in it, and put a grate in it so that animals won't climb down it. Since the pipe is black, it will absorb more solar energy and heat it up. Likewise, the air inside of the pipe will also heat up. Hot air rises. When the air in the pipe begins to rise up, it creates a suction effect that pulls air up out of the house itself.

On another portion or portions of the house, there is also great air intake. There's always somewhere that is relatively cool—this could be in the shade or from your geothermal system. Since the hot air at the chimney is creating a suction effect and pulling air through the house, the new air will come in through the cold vents, or the geothermal system does add cool air into the home.

These systems are very different from your traditional methods. Some people have great success with these, and others don't. It's certainly something that requires thought and planning to maximize its benefits.

The major drawback of this design is that you cannot retrofit a building—it has to be designed as an integral part of the architecture.

Solar Fans

You can't go wrong with fans. Fans are cheap and don't require a lot of power. In fact, when you need to fan the most, the sun is usually shining. Solar fans are often a very good option. Fans inside of an animal's space will help keep them cool and also help ventilate any smells.

It's also recommended that solar fans be placed inside any greenhouse that you build. This will help regulate the temperature inside. Plants like it hot, but they don't like it too hot.

If you're clever about it, you can find cool spaces near your house, using a fan to blow the cool air in and a different fan to push the hot air out. You can run a pipe or something through a shady area for your intake fan. You can also run an output fan at a higher level where the hottest air goes.

This is a very low-tech solution. We would not recommend using this alone. This is a good way to supplement any other cooling system that you have, but it probably won't be sufficient on its own, just like rainwater is insufficient to cover all of your water needs.

Sun Oven and Outdoor Fires

On a hot day, you do not want to be cooking food indoors. All the heat produced will just make your home that much hotter. Cooking outside is a great solution. It's no accident that summer is the grilling season.

Sun Oven is the perfect product to reduce the indoor heat. It's a box with a couple open sides and reflective surfaces on the inside. This works exactly as you would expect. The sun reflects and cooks whatever you place inside the Sun Oven. It's not fast—it works like a slow cooker, which makes it great for stews and chili.

Chapter 7:

Off-Grid Waste

Management

Waste management is very important and also one of the things we think about least when considering living off the grid. When you live on a plumbing and sewage system and have garbage collection regularly, you don't have to think about this very much. However, when waste disposal becomes your job to take care of, you will understand how important it really is.

DO NOT dump your septic waste on your property. It is gross, illegal, and dangerous. We're sure most of my readers already know this, but for the rest of you, don't do this. We don't care if animals use the wilderness as their restroom.

Trash and Composting

Any leftover material that you are throwing out such as scraps from dinner, leftover food that goes bad, or little bits of meat on the bones of ribs you cooked the night before can be used to fuel your garden.

There's no need to waste perfectly good material. Even things like coffee grounds, eggshells, and ash can be great in a garden. You will definitely want to have a separate place to dispose of compostable materials and set that aside. If you own pigs, they are always happy to have any scraps or leftovers that you are done with.

If you're doing any gardening, and you probably are, you are going to definitely want a compost pile.

There are two kinds of composting: hot and cold. Cold is as simple as taking the waste and putting it in a container or pile and letting them decompose.

Hot composting requires more work, but it speeds up the process. When the weather is warm, you can speed it up so that it is done in a month or two. To get faster composting, you're going to need oxygen, water, carbon, and nitrogen. All of these things will help feed the microorganisms that will consume the matter, speeding up the rate of decay.

You can also speed this up by purchasing worms. You won't be using the night crawlers that you buy for fishing or any other worm. Specifically, you need red worms, also sometimes called red wigglers. These are not hard to find. Any place that has a decent gardening supply section should be able to help you out.

Whatever the bio trash you are using, you are also going to want to add nitrogen-rich material. This would include grass trimmings, leaves, tree branches, newspaper, hay, cardboard, and wood chips. Any of these materials should be mixed in with the material you are composting.

If you aren't getting much rain, you're going to need to water the pile regularly just like it's a garden of trash. You're not trying to get totally soaked—you just want to add enough water that the microorganisms can do their job. However, don't add so much that you drown your red wigglers. If you can put your hand inside of it and feel it's producing a lot of heat, you are doing it right.

About every week or so, you should turn your pile over and let it mix around. To do this with the shovel or pitchfork, just keep it moving. Make sure it's getting oxygen in the center. At this point, it should be getting very hot, up to 150 degrees.

Your compost is done when it stops putting out lots of heat. It should start looking like dirt again. At that point, it is perfect for your garden, so go ahead and transplant that dirt and all your red wigglers into their new home.

Trash

Anything that isn't compostable, biodegradable, or burnable, such as plastic, should be placed in a container and set aside. Since you don't have a trash removal service coming to your location, you will need to take it to a dump yourself or schedule someone to come and get it. Hopefully, the amount of this kind of waste will diminish over time, and these trips will become less frequent.

Burn

Some things are perfectly fine to burn such as wood or cotton, cloth, paper towel rolls, and dryer lint. Again, just like the water, don't set anything on fire that is going to create toxicity. Don't try burning plastic or metal with paint on it or something else that you wouldn't want to breathe.

When burning things, always do so responsibly. Don't start a fire if you live in a dry climate during a dry spell. In certain places like Wyoming and Colorado, starting fires can be very risky. If you are going to use a burn barrel, just be careful, and be sure to have a fire extinguisher close by.

We're sure we sound like a broken record but here it is: Make sure it is legal to burn your trash. Different places have different rules. If you're deep enough back from the road, probably no one will see you, but it needs to be said.

Gray Water

Gray water is dirty water from your sink or shower—this isn't toilet water. It's simple enough to get rid of so long as you aren't using soaps and detergents with harmful chemicals. If you are using all-natural stuff to wash your body and your dishes, then this water can simply be grounded out of the house and dropped onto the soil working to be reabsorbed by the earth. Be sure that nothing you deposit is going to be harmful and harm the plants or wildlife out there or be something that you don't want anything to do with the groundwater.

Make sure nothing that goes into the gray water is harmful. You can check all your labels and investigate if you have any doubts. If you are using detergents and soaps that are harmful, you can always put those into a septic system.

Depending on how you set up your water, there are many ways to capture your gray water and separate it from your septic system. It can be simply diverted into a bucket. As simple as that sounds, that's completely viable. Gray water could also be diverted toward a particular use that you have in mind. For example, gray water, provided that it is clean enough that it won't hurt plants, could potentially be diverted into the yard to be reabsorbed by the soil. If you are especially confident of the quality of your gray water, you could even divert it to your garden to water plants.

Gray water that is dirty can also be used for flushing toilets, washing your clothes, or washing your car. That is a good way to get multiple uses out of one batch of water and get much more efficient use for it. That's definitely more preferable than dumping it in a septic system.

Septic System

Probably the most popular option is to install a septic system. If you have any kind of internal plumbing in your home, you are definitely going to need this. A septic system is a gigantic tank buried underground just like a water tank, but instead of holding water, it holds everything you flush down the toilet. We don't want the septic system boiling, and we don't want it freezing. Either is going to be a worse disaster than bursting the water tanks, believe me.

Tanks have a hatch, and you will need to periodically have a waste removal truck come and suck out of the waste that is stored there. Depending on the size of your tank and how many people live in your home, this could be only once every few years.

Outhouse

Outhouses are a very old way of doing things. They don't require any water and are very easy to build. It may not be surprising to know that most people don't want to use an outhouse. To use the bathroom you're going to have to leave your house, and if it's in the dead of winter, that's not too fun.

If you don't want to live a life within our house, they might just be useful as a start-up way to have a restroom until you are completely building a more permanent one. If your properties are particularly large, you might find that putting in an outhouse at the far end will be helpful when walking around so that you don't have to hike all the way back to your home for number two.

Composting Toilet

This isn't very attractive for everyone but it's actually really great. A composting toilet does not use water. If you remember from the earlier chapter on setting up your water, toilet flushes account for a huge amount of the water that you go through.

Composting toilets can be purchased or built from scratch. You won't need a septic system, so long as you have a good means of disposing of your gray water.

Essentially, this is a system to dump in a bucket and turn your own waste into human compost. Yes, that sounds pretty gross, but it's not as bad as you think. You save a lot of water, and it's very eco-friendly.

Your waste is caught into a bucket with sawdust. The sawdust works a lot like cat litter, it absorbs your waste and also cuts down on the smell. The drier, the better. Some have two separate chambers: one for urine and one for feces.

In your home, you're going to want a fan system to ventilate odors out of your home. Some water mixed with vinegar in a spray bottle can also help a lot.

When you've got a full bucket, haul it out to your composting heap. This is by far the greenest option of all of them. If you are particularly concerned about conservation, this is your best bet.

One way to know who your real friends are is to invite them for a soak in a hot tub hooked up to a compost heat system, heated using your own human manure.

An Outline to Start Your

New Home

This is the order of operations to get your homestead off the ground. You can use this as a general outline or like a worksheet, a place to get your mind moving and to get the process of planning moving.

Step One: Make a Decision

This is the biggest step of all. Simply choose if you want to do it. You will need to consider if this is good for your family overall. Make sure that everyone involved understands and is happy to participate. If you have a spouse and children, they need to be okay with all this stuff, too.

Step Two: Planning

The more planning you do, the easier and smoother all the rest of the steps are.

- Figure out your budget.

- Research locations.

- Choose a state and county.

- If you are moving far away, you will have to figure out work if you can't do it remotely—that might mean looking for a new job.

- Calculate your power consumption; estimate how much power you can generate.

- Calculate your water consumption; estimate how much water you can produce.

You want to have an estimate of all the material costs. If there's going to be an interruption to your income, that's going to have to be figured out. There's the price of land and if you live in a state with property taxes.

You also want a buffer room. It is a sure thing that things will go wrong. That's not an off-grid thing, that's a life thing. You might make an error and wire up your electrical system wrong and accidentally torch your inverter. You might have horrendous weather that slows you down. Maybe a clever fox finds their way into your chicken coop. Things always go wrong, and they take time, energy, and money to make them right.

Step Three: Find Land

Once all the other considerations have been weighed, and you know what you are looking for, go find it and buy it.

The two most important things are:

- a place where you are actually allowed to live off-grid without too much interference from red tape and regulation.

- a source of water.

If you are going to need a deep well, get that scheduled and have them come to do that early. If they can't find water, and there is no other good source, this spot is a bust. There's no reason to sink more money or energy into it. Provided that goes well (no pun intended), carry on!

If you don't have a mailbox, you are going to want to get a P.O. box so that you can receive mail and packages.

Step Four: Make a Shelter

Move to your new place. You're going to need a place to sleep. It's fine to start with something small like a camper, a trailer, or even a van if you can stand it. It's definitely recommended that you start in the spring when the temperature is just starting to warm up, and you have more warm months to get started.

If you have a family, they don't all have to come at this point. They can hang back while you get things prepared. It might require some trips back and forth; it might be a process.

Step Four can stay with the temporary place or you can build a more permanent system as you go along. Step Four also fits between every other step.

Step Five: Get Your Baseline

You have a temporary shelter. You also need electricity, water, and food.

Get yourself a gas-powered generator. This is a temporary power source, just until you can get your sustainable system operational.

You need water. You can have it delivered or you can haul it yourself.

Food will be the same grocery-bought stuff you always use.

You'll also need a place to relieve yourself. If you have a trailer or a camper, that's covered. If not, you will need a bucket full of sawdust or an outhouse for the time being.

Garbage can be put in a can or bags and taken to the dump as needed.

You need to get some kind of communication system up as quickly as possible. Depending on how far out your new home is, you may not be able to catch a signal. You can buy a signal booster and attach it to a small tower. That can give you a lot more range. If that doesn't do the trick, consider getting a satellite Internet service.

You're going to want to be able to call for help in an emergency, check the weather, and look up how-to guides when you run into things you don't know how to do. Communication is mandatory.

You now have your baseline. You have all the basic needs covered. As this project continues, each one of those will be replaced with a sustainable system.

Step Six: Electricity

Set up your electrical system. You need your solar panels and/or wind turbines up. You need to get them hooked up safely.

You need a location to house the power system. That probably means building a shed to house everything away from the elements, especially water. Run your connections from your power source. Hook up your AC inverter, batteries, charge controller, fuses, bus bars, etc. Get that all wired up. Contact an electrician if you need to. Safety first!

Step Seven: Water

Now that you have power, you can operate pumps. Once you can have operational pumps, you can get water. Your next task is to hook up to your water source. If you have tanks/cisterns, pipes, and filters ready to go, you are in business. If you have a house built, that means hooking that up. Life just got a lot easier. Also, you can now heat your water, which is a big deal if you've been living without it for a little while.

Step Eight: Waste

Now that you have water, you can hook that up to a septic system. Congratulations if you were using a bucket before because you can now use a toilet!

Step Nine: Start Your Farm

Now that you have working water, you can start your farm and your composting.

Set up a garden and/or build a greenhouse, and get started on any planting.

If you are keeping animals, build them a coop, barn, fenced-in area, or whatever they need.

You are really rolling now!

Step Ten: Do Whatever You Want

You should have all the basic ingredients for self-sustenance: shelter, electricity, water, and food. You can use a toilet and take a shower.

These may not be completely up and running quite yet—you may have hiccups. If necessary, there's no shame in supplementing yourself with visits to the store if you need to.

Where you go from here is entirely up to you. You may find that you want to start upgrading some new systems. You may find that one of the systems you've already built can be built better or optimized.

All the necessities are taken care of. What you do next is whatever you want to do!

Conclusion

Now that we're at the end of the book, you may have started working out a rough sketch of the home you want to build. Maybe you've got your ideal state narrowed down to a few. You've got some ideas about what your home will look like, how you think you can power it, and how to supply water into it.

That's good—get that rough sketch, but don't try to put the ink down on this paper in your imagination just yet. Once you get started, there are going to be a lot of changes and adaptations that you will make along the way. Don't get too hung up on a perfect and idealized version of your homestead. Instead, you and the land should meet each other halfway and figure it out together.

This one book is not going to be nearly enough to teach you everything that you should or want to know. There is a lot more to raising chickens and growing tomatoes than we could possibly cover in these few pages. One of the most important things you should do is continue learning.

When you decide you want to set up your own AC converter, but you don't know the first thing about electricity, you're going to have to read another book about that. Just absorb as much as you can. There are so many other homesteaders and off-grid people out there. There are many forums full of people that are eager to talk to you and share tips. There are countless websites full of great information that can teach you a lot and point you in the right direction.

We know that you're curious about moving off-grid, but at this stage, you're probably more than curious. If you didn't like the idea or didn't sound like it was for you, you probably would have stopped reading this book halfway through earlier, but because you read it from the front to the back, you're still interested.

If you are so interested and have the means and opportunity, We would definitely recommend that you take this on. This is not something we would encourage a half-interested person to do, but if you have made it to the conclusion of this book, you are feeling excited, and you are thinking about all the different projects that you could do and only things you want to learn, then we say follow that instinct. Take it to its ultimate conclusion. Find your own independence, self-reliance, and environmental consideration, and build yourself a place that you will be happy and free.

One Last Thing

We spend so much of our modern lives making things that only exist virtually. Many of us spend a third of our day operating computers. Money people collate tables and leverage financial instruments to make money. Software engineers write complex algebraic formulas to develop a cell phone app. Marketing people look at charts and figures that tell them what people want, without ever talking to people.

So much of what we do isn't material. It exists as an abstraction. People are aching to do something real, tangible, and right here. You'll see it in little ways.

You see people taking on knitting as a hobby, which was formerly considered something that old women do, but young women have suddenly taken an interest in crocheting and other crafts—things that require physical contact.

People are suddenly taking up hobbies like ax throwing and bowhunting.

People get on the Internet and look at videos of people building furniture from scratch.

People start brewing their own beer at home.

People seem to be yearning for another era where people worked with their hands, and when they were done working, there was something tangible in front of them—something that they could be proud of. Instead of working a job and seeing numbers appear in a bank account so they can purchase objects made on the other side of the world, they just want to make something themselves and have it. They want to see the fruits of their own labor and hold on to it like a trophy or a memento—some kind of physical reminder that they can be proud of.

You can feel it too, can't you? Building a life off-grid is not weird. What's weird is living in tiny concrete boxes, stacked hundreds of feet tall, in a gray, concrete place where every day, you see thousands of people walk past you, and you don't know a single one of them.

If you want to try something new—if you want to craft the environment into a place just for you—then you are like many others. Many of them are less smart and talented than you are. If they can do it, you can, too.

References

Average Annual Precipitation for Missouri. (n.d.). Current Results.
https://www.currentresults.com/Weather/Missouri/average-yearly-precipitation.php

Buri, R. (2017). Solar-roof-solar-energy. In *pixabay.com*.
https://cdn.pixabay.com/photo/2017/08/21/20/29/solar-2666770_960_720.jpg

Cloud, B. (2018). Lake in forest. In *unsplash.com*.
https://images.unsplash.com/photo-1542849922-a7e0aeb0ff84?ixlib=rb-1.2.1&ixid=MnwxMjA3fDB8MHxwaG90by1wYWdlfHx8fGVufDB8fHx8&auto=format&fit=crop&w=1534&q=80

Dais, W. (2011). chicken-coop-farm-chickens-coop. In *pixabay.com*.
https://cdn.pixabay.com/photo/2014/05/14/08/02/chicken-coop-343942_960_720.jpg

Ellis, K. (2018). Triangle house. In *unsplash.com*.
https://images.unsplash.com/photo-1525113990976-399835c43838?ixid=MnwxMjA3fDB8MHxwaG90by1wYWdlfHx8fGVufDB8fHx8&ixlib=rb-1.2.1&auto=format&fit=crop&w=700&q=80

Giannatti, D. (2019). Outhouse door. In *unsplash.com*. https://images.unsplash.com/photo-1548097751-193b78ef6823?ixid=MnwxMjA3fDB8MHxwaG90by1wYWdlfHx8fGVufDB8fHx8&ixlib=rb-1.2.1&auto=format&fit=crop&w=639&q=80

Glenn, K. (2018). Green dome near brown wooden dock. In *unsplash.com*. https://images.unsplash.com/photo-1521401830884-6c03c1c87ebb?ixlib=rb-1.2.1&ixid=MnwxMjA3fDB8MHxwaG90by1wYWdlfHx8fGVufDB8fHx8&auto=format&fit=crop&w=1500&q=80

Gomez, J. (2019). Wood stove. In *unsplash.com*. https://images.unsplash.com/photo-1564848534637-f57f9b1eb36e?ixlib=rb-1.2.1&ixid=MnwxMjA3fDB8MHxwaG90by1wYWdlfHx8fGVufDB8fHx8&auto=format&fit=crop&w=632&q=80

Gruebner, O., Rapp, M. A., Adli, M., Kluge, U., Galea, S., & Heinz, A. (2017). Cities and Mental Health. *Deutsches Arzteblatt international*, *114*(8), 121–127. https://doi.org/10.3238/arztebl.2017.0121

How We Use Water. (n.d.). United States Environmental Protection Agency (EPA). https://www.epa.gov/watersense/how-we-use-water

Jesus, J. (n.d.). Photo-of-man-standing-surrounded-by-green-leaf-plants. In *pexels.com*. https://images.pexels.com/photos/1084540/pexels-photo-1084540.jpeg?auto=compress&cs=tinysrgb&dpr=2&h=650&w=940

Lechner, G. (2020). Black and white wooden house. In *unsplash.com*. https://images.unsplash.com/photo-1580856942656-d4416b6e5c2e?ixlib=rb-1.2.1&ixid=MnwxMjA3fDB8MHxwaG90by1wYWdlfHx8fGVufDB8fHx8&auto=format&fit=crop&w=1563&q=80

Living, O. G. (2020, February 26). *How to go off grid for $10k or less*. Off Grid Living. https://offgridliving.net/go-off-grid-10k/

PublicDomainPictures. (2010). Clean-countryside-drink-garden. In *pixabay.com*. https://cdn.pixabay.com/photo/2012/03/03/22/59/clean-21479_960_720.jpg

Timmer, K. (2019). Brown wood house. In *unsplash.com*. https://images.unsplash.com/photo-1568659585069-facb248c4935?ixlib=rb-1.2.1&ixid=MnwxMjA3fDB8MHxwaG90by1wYWdlfHx8fGVufDB8fHx8&auto=format&fit=crop&w=1500&q=80